DBT, CBT, and Play Therapy Toolbox for Children and Adolescents

Over 200 Worksheets and Activities to Address Anxiety, Depression, Trauma, Boundaries, Relationships, Self-Esteem, Motivation, Family Dynamics, and More

Amanda K. Crowder, MSW, LCSW

Julianna Elsworth, MSW, LCSW

Anastasia Harmeyer, MSW, LCSW, LCAS

DBT, CBT, and Play Therapy Toolbox for Children and Adolescents
Copyright © 2023 by Amanda K. Crowder, Julianna Elsworth, and Anastasia Harmeyer

Published by
PESI Publishing, Inc.
3839 White Ave
Eau Claire, WI 54703

Cover and interior design by Emily Dyer
Editing by Jenessa Jackson, PhD

ISBN 9781683737049 (print)
ISBN 9781683737063 (ePDF)
ISBN 9781683737056 (ePUB)

PESI Publishing
pesipublishing.com

Table of Contents

Introduction for Adults

Child and adolescent development is far from predictable. It is a time that can cause confusion and conflict for adults and youth alike. From the elementary-aged child struggling to understand healthy boundaries, to the teenager exhibiting risky sexual behavior, or the middle school adolescent engaging in self-harm, childhood is a developmental age fraught with treatment challenges. When working with these children and teens, it can sometimes be difficult to find the most effective ways of interacting. It can feel like no matter what we say or how we say it, our efforts are met with resistance. And although we *think* we understand (we've all been there ourselves after all!), we often walk away feeling like we've been unhelpful.

That's where this workbook comes in. We'll touch on how to navigate topics that can be uncomfortable, behaviors that are disturbing, and experiences that no one wants to go through alone. We will review and provide solutions to key issues that children and adolescents face on a daily basis that are typically not found in other therapeutic workbooks, including self-sabotage, lack of motivation, boundary concerns, healthy relationships, self-harm, and sexuality—just to name a few. Utilizing experiential and collaborative activities, we will go beyond teaching "basic" skills by asking in-depth questions that challenge kids to explore further within themselves and their family system. It provides straightforward, doable solutions for some of the most challenging problems children and adolescents face.

What's In This Book?

In this workbook, you'll find a variety of worksheets, activities, and exercises that teach kids the emotional, behavioral, and social skills needed to address the unique issues that arise during this developmental stage. Grounded within the principles of cognitive behavioral therapy (CBT), dialectical behavioral therapy (DBT), play therapy, and more, these activities target a variety of diagnoses, such as generalized anxiety, depression, disruptive mood dysregulation, sexual behaviors of concern, posttraumatic stress disorder, and adjustment disorders.

This workbook is divided into 10 sections, with each section coinciding with a specific problem area and accompanying activities intended to address each area. We intentionally formatted the book this way so it would be easy to navigate in terms of problem and solution. In addition, exercises are categorized by age range, with certain activities targeted for younger kids and others for older adolescents. However, all of the exercises can be modified and adapted for all types of youth, as we wanted to make this workbook practical and applicable, especially knowing the unpredictability that arises in our day-to-day lives. The topics and activities don't have to be completed in any particular order—instead, they can be used as needed whenever issues arise. This setup is intended for flexibility, as we understand that the challenges children and adolescents face are rarely predictable. We also encourage creativity when using this workbook. No one child, adolescent, identified concern, or family system is the same.

Whom Is This Book For?

As adults, we play a crucial role in a child's developmental journey into adulthood, regardless of whether our role in that child's life is as a professional or as another person of significance. Therefore, this workbook is designed for trusted adults who work with children and adolescents in any capacity, including psychologists, teachers, social workers, mental health therapists, school counselors, and even parents or caregivers. Certain activities are intended specifically for the school setting, whereas others may be more useful to those working in inpatient, outpatient, residential, or community-based settings. In addition, we've included several parent and caregiver tools, since we know these adults play a crucial role in a child's healing process. This workbook is designed to be used alone or collaboratively within an established clinical context, so kids can also use this book on their own or with the support of a trusted adult.

We have worked hard to create something new, innovative, and different from what you will find within the current market. And we would like to welcome and thank those adults who are purchasing this workbook in the spirit of supporting a child or adolescent. Whether you are a parent, caregiver, counselor, teacher, or any other trusted adult, it is your relationship with this youth that will yield the most important results. It is our hope that this workbook can provide resources and activities to enhance that relationship and create a space for healing. Our goal is to give you the necessary tools to dig deeper and to assist kids in having a better understanding of themselves, their families, their social relationships, and the world around them.

Introduction for Kids

It's not easy being a kid. Sometimes it seems like everyone else knows how to deal with a problem except you. It can feel like adults are in charge of your life—always telling you what to do, what's right and wrong, and even sometimes who you "should" or "shouldn't" be. It can be difficult adjusting to all of the changes happening during this time in your life, which makes sense because your body and brain are growing so quickly!

On top of these personal changes, you may also be dealing with some hard or challenging situations, such as family problems, difficulty making friends, or experiences that are scary, bad, or uncomfortable. Although these experiences can create many different feelings—including confusion, excitement, sadness, nervousness, and so many more—we want you to know that these experiences are *very* normal and that lots of kids deal with these same issues.

We know it's not always easy to talk about yourself, your family, or topics that can be uncomfortable or confusing. But our hope is that this workbook will provide activities for you to explore who you are and who you want to be. It will teach you skills that you can keep in your "toolbox" so you can use them whenever you need to throughout the rest of your life. And even though it can be hard to talk about some of these topics, you can do it!

As you make your way through this workbook, we encourage you to do so with the help of a trusted adult. This can be a parent, caregiver, teacher, therapist, school counselor, or any adult you feel comfortable talking to about your life. Although lots of kids are hesitant to talk about their thoughts, feelings, and behaviors, they usually feel better once they talk with someone. Just remember that the most important person in this process is YOU.

Welcome! We look forward to working with you on this adventure and journey!

Definitions

Throughout this book, we will use a variety of terms, so we want to make sure you understand what these words mean and how they are used in this book. The following list includes terms we felt important to highlight. Refer back to these definitions as needed, and as you work your way through the activities with a trusted adult.

- **Mindfulness:** The best way to describe mindfulness is the skill of being present and in the moment. When you're mindful, you're not thinking about the past or the future. You're not getting stuck in your head with your own thoughts. You're not thinking about what happened yesterday or what you need to do tomorrow. Instead, you're just in the moment—right here, right now.

- **Vulnerability:** Vulnerability involves doing something that stretches you outside of your comfort zone. It means being honest with yourself and showing your true self to others. Although vulnerability is often seen as a weakness—as it can be scary and uncomfortable to open up—it is actually a measurement of courage. For example, sometimes when you become angry at a friend, you want to just shut down or ignore them. But being vulnerable would involve having a conversation with that friend and talking about why you are angry.

- **Emotionally present:** When you are emotionally present, you bring attention to your feelings and allow yourself to experience them completely in your body and mind. (Believe it or not, we often try *not* to feel our emotions!) When you are aware of your feelings, you are able to use them to help you take actions or make decisions.

- **Sensory experience:** A sensory experience involves any situation where you use your five senses: sight, sound, smell, taste, and touch. When you have a sensory experience, you bring awareness to your senses and think about how your body feels in that moment.

- **Resistance:** Resistance involves knowing what you need to do but not wanting to do it. In other words, it involves pushing back on what is being asked or requested of you.

- **Judgment:** A judgment is a thought that is not based on fact. It is your opinion. Sometimes we have positive judgments, and other times we have negative judgments. When we refer to judgments throughout this workbook, we'll typically be referring to negative judgments, as these are the ones you'll need to bring to your attention.

- **Empathy:** When you have empathy, you are able to understand what someone else is thinking and feeling. It is the action of putting yourself in someone else's shoes and seeing things from their point of view.

- **Boundaries:** A boundary describes a line that separates what is you and what is not you. In other words, it provides a space between your own personal values and everything else. Most people believe that boundaries need to involve a very dark, thick, hard line—but that's not always the case! Sometimes boundaries need to be that powerful, but other times they can change as the things around us change. Boundaries can make you feel selfish, but when you feel that way, you're doing it right!

- **Adjustment/transition:** An adjustment or transition is something that involves a big life change (or even a bunch of smaller changes). This can include starting a new school, moving to a different neighborhood, your parents getting divorced, introducing a new sibling to the family, and so many more. An adjustment is something you get to define for yourself, so it only matters whether the change feels big or small to *you* and no one else.

Creating Space, Building Rapport, and Overcoming Resistance

Building a relationship can have its challenges, especially when working with children, adolescents, and families. Sometimes you are met with resistance and willfulness, which is why we find it imperative that you meet your client where they are. We understand this may sound cliché, but we find that it is necessary if you want to create a safe space where therapeutic work can happen.

Space is an important concept within the therapeutic environment. It is what you, as the treatment provider, and your client share together. This environment or "space" allows your client to have difficult and challenging conversations and to also feel all the tough feelings. We also understand that some of the clients you work with are resistant and don't want to be in therapy ("I don't have a problem!"—we've all heard that one before). However, the ability to build rapport is one of the greatest predictors of treatment outcomes. Without a relationship, there is no trust or sense of safety. And without this, there isn't much work that can take place.

Therefore, in this section, we include activities to help you get to know your client and to allow your client the opportunity to get to know you. This allows them to have a little control within the therapeutic space. It can assist in motivating them as well, as they will realize they don't only have to talk about themselves this way. We further address motivation with mindfulness exercises and worksheets. These tools are the starting point to any new therapeutic relationship.

Throughout this book, we want you to remember that you are the tool and your client is the contractor. Some contractors can get the job done in a day, and some take time and lots of steps. As always, it is important to meet the client where they are—full heartedly. Let them guide their own treatment. Sometimes the work we do is about planting seeds and not necessarily "fixing" the problem. Take it slow and always put the client first. If they are still coming to see you, then there is work that is being done.

Mind-Full Box

Sometimes our feelings get too big when something hard happens, and sometimes they can get too big for no reason at all. When this happens, imagine putting all your negative thoughts, fears, worries, and feelings into a box that is safe. This box is a place where you can hold those hard things until you are ready and able to deal with them. You get to decide what goes in the box and how to keep the things inside safe and organized. On the next page, you'll find a box where you can store these hard things. Use any kind of art materials (markers, crayons, etc.) to decorate your box any way you'd like to make it your own. Then follow these steps:

1. Think about something upsetting or stressful. Imagine placing it inside the box and closing the lid.

2. Pay attention to the positive feeling (e.g., relief, safety, lightness) that happens when you imagine placing it in the box.

3. Alternate tapping each of your feet as you take a few deep breaths. Make sure you focus on the positive feeling, knowing you have this box to hold your hard feelings.

   Do you notice anything different now? How do you feel?

EXPERIENTIAL USE

Find any kind of container with a cover that you would like to use as your box. It could be an old shoebox, a cardboard container, or a storage dish—anything that has a lid will work just fine! Be as creative as you want and decorate the box in a way that makes it yours and makes it feel safe. Use scraps of paper to write down hard things you are dealing with, or find items to represent the hard things, then place these in the box and follow the steps outlined in this worksheet.

Aware and Care

As we start our work together, it is important for you to check in with yourself regularly to make sure you are taking care of your mind and body. Here are some self-care tips that you might find helpful in taking care of yourself. Place a check mark by the ones you find the most helpful.

☐ **Check in with your breathing.** Practice breathing as if you are standing tall like a toy soldier. As you breathe in and out, see if you can slow your breathing down. Can you find the rhythm of your heartbeat and your breath?

☐ **Stretch!** If you find yourself distracted—or you just need to move your body a little— take some time to stretch your muscles.

☐ **Stay hydrated.** Make sure you are drinking plenty of water throughout the day.

☐ **Practice being mindful.** Notice if your mind starts to wander. If it does, what is it that's distracting you? What are you thinking about? Is there any noise that is catching your attention?

☐ **Remember to use your five senses (sight, sound, smell, taste, and touch).** Find one thing that you can hear, taste, touch, smell, and see in the space around you.

☐ **Be curious about your feelings.** Notice whatever you are feeling without labeling the feelings as "good" or "bad."

☐ **Set a goal for the day.** Who do you want to be today? What do you want to focus on? Remind yourself of your goal throughout the day.

Setting Expectations

This worksheet is all about setting expectations for your treatment! In other words, it's to help you figure out what it is that *you* want out of this process. It's a place where we can talk about what I expect from you, what you need from me, and especially what you need to feel supported by the trusted adults in your life.

Expectations for you:

- Be honest!

- Be open to feedback and ideas.

- Work hard in *your* treatment!

- Complete in-session and out-of-session assignments when asked to do so.

- _____

- _____

- _____

Expectations for me (*treatment provider*):

- Validate, understand, and be empathetic.

- _____

- _____

- _____

Expectations for trusted adults:

- Listen. Don't try to fix anything—just listen.

- Acknowledge your role in the problem.

- Validate, understand, and be empathetic.

- _____

- _____

- _____

Ideas to Think About:

This process is all about *you*. Think about the last time you felt heard and listened to. What was it about that experience that made that true for you?

_____

_____

_____

_____

Think about what it is that you need. Are you doing this work for you or someone else? If you're doing it for someone else, is there any part of you that is also doing it for you? If so, find that part and speak from its point of view.

_____

_____

_____

_____

When you feel like giving up, what will keep you going? What are the words of encouragement that you need to hear?

_____

_____

_____

_____

What makes you feel safe, both physically and emotionally?

_____

_____

_____

_____

Music Playlist

Ages
10+

Music is a great way to express how we feel. It can help us describe who we are and what we enjoy. The kind of music you listen to helps others get to know you! Make a list of your favorite songs. Share the artist, the lyrics you like best, and how the song makes you feel when you listen to it.

1. Song: _____

    Artist: _____

    Lyrics: _____

    Feeling: _____

2. Song: _____

    Artist: _____

    Lyrics: _____

    Feeling: _____

3. Song: _____

    Artist: _____

    Lyrics: _____

    Feeling: _____

QUESTIONS

• How does the music you like to listen to change depending on how you feel?
• In what ways can music affect your emotions?
• Describe a time when music helped you get through a difficult time.

This Is Me

Work with your treatment provider or trusted adult to fill in the following blanks. You can say your responses out loud or write them down here. Then let your treatment provider have a turn—this isn't only for them to get to know you, but for you to get to know them!

- My favorite color is _____.

- A time I remember is _____.

- I feel safest when _____.

- I like to eat _____.

- At home I like to _____.

- My favorite time of the year is _____.

- My favorite holiday is _____.

- Something that most people don't know about me is _____.

- I am happy when _____.

- When I listen to music, I _____.

- I talk to my friends about _____.

- My favorite movie is _____.

- Sometimes I get sad when _____.

- My middle name is _____.

- If I was an animal, I would be a _____.

- My family makes me feel _____.

- My friends say _____.

- One thing my mom says all the time is _____.

- One thing my dad says all the time is _____.

- I always try to remember _____.

- I wish _____.

- _____.

Would You Rather?

Playing a game can be a great way to build relationships, and it also makes it easier to talk about things that are sometimes hard to share with others. In each row, circle which statement you would rather have. Don't forget: The only rule is that you have to choose!

Be stuck inside all day reading books	**OR**	Be outside engaged in physical activity
Go to the beach for vacation	**OR**	Go to the mountains for vacation
Live where it is always cold	**OR**	Live where it is always hot
Get one big present	**OR**	Get lots of small presents
See everything in black and white	**OR**	See everything blurry
Be really good at one thing	**OR**	Be okay at many things
Live without a cell phone	**OR**	Live without a car
Live alone	**OR**	Live with a bunch of people
Only able to wear black	**OR**	Only able to wear bright colors
Change your personality	**OR**	Change your appearance
Live without music	**OR**	Live without TV
Have lots of siblings	**OR**	Be the only child
Scroll through Instagram	**OR**	Scroll through TikTok
Be extremely smart	**OR**	Be extremely talented
Live without video games	**OR**	Live without sugar
Uncontrollably burp	**OR**	Uncontrollably laugh
Have a few close friends	**OR**	Have lots of acquaintances
Have to eat your favorite food every day	**OR**	Never have your favorite food again

U-Pick

This list includes many activities that we can do during our time together. Put a check mark by the ones you may be interested in! We will keep this list to use for future ideas. There are also spaces for you to add activities you think would be fun.

Games

☐ Candy Land®

☐ UNO®

☐ Sorry!®

☐ Phase 10®

☐ War (card game)

☐ Would You Rather

☐ _____

Whiteboard

☐ Hangman

☐ Pictionary™

☐ Practice drawing

☐ Tic-Tac-Toe

☐ _____

Art

☐ Color

☐ Draw

☐ Make beaded crafts

☐ Play with modeling clay

☐ Paint

☐ _____

Ages
8+

All Bottled Up

Opening up can be tough, especially when you don't feel like you need help or someone to talk to. You may feel like someone else will tell others what you share, or you might believe that others are actually to blame.

Use the space in the bottle to write down why you are here and what makes it tough for you to be here. As you fill in the bottle, think about why it is hard to talk about your feelings. What makes change hard? Why it is hard to admit that something might be wrong? When you're done, you and your treatment provider can "break the bottle" and start building trust.

QUESTIONS

- What do we need to break the bottle and break down some of the barriers you identified?
- Has anything ever made it more difficult for you to open and connect to others?
- What is one first step you could take to opening up?

Validation in Resistance

Opening up can be challenging—and sometimes you just don't want to for one reason or another. You're absolutely right in thinking that this is hard work! However, it's important to figure out how to move through whatever is keeping you stuck so you can move forward in your treatment. Use this checklist to identify any obstacles that are getting in the way.

☐ It is hard to talk about this problem.

☐ I am embarrassed I have this problem.

☐ I'm not strong enough to "get over" this problem.

☐ I don't want to talk about the problem.

☐ I've tried talking about this problem before and it didn't help.

☐ You're not going to believe me.

☐ You're not going to be on my side.

☐ I have a hard time trusting others.

☐ I'm scared something bad will happen if I talk about my problem.

☐ I don't feel safe talking about my problem.

☐ I don't want to get over the problem.

☐ This problem defines who I am.

☐ I don't have a problem.

☐ I'm only here for _____.

☐ I don't want to get anyone in trouble.

QUESTIONS

- If you could work on one thing, what would that be?
- What feels safe here with me, and what does not feel safe?
- Are there any changes I can make to help you feel safe? For example, are there any items or objects—like a stuffed animal, blanket, or pillow—I can get you?
- Would you be willing to talk with someone else about this problem? If so, whom?
- What if I told you we can take this one step at a time? How does that change things?
- Is there any piece of the problem you are willing to talk about? If so, what?
- Is there anyone you do trust? If so, how did you learn to trust them?

What Impacts Your Motivation?

There are a lot of things that can negatively impact your motivation. What affects one person may have very little impact on someone else. The following list shows some of the factors that can impact how motivated you feel. This can change day-to-day. For each factor, consider how it is impacting you right now and rate it on a scale of 0 to 10 (with 0 being "this does not affect my motivation at all" and 10 being "this affects my motivation *a lot*").

Factors	Rate (0–10)	Factors	Rate (0–10)
Friendships		Romantic relationships	
Physical health		Living situation	
How I feel about myself		Recent failures	
School		Fears	
Family		Responsibilities (chores, job, etc.)	
Money		Structure (too much or lack of)	
Stress		Drugs or alcohol	
Peer pressure		Other:	

QUESTIONS

- Which factors did you rate as having the biggest effect on your motivation? How do these factors get in the way?
- What prevents you from working on these factors and making changes?
- How can others support you in improving your motivation?

Keep, Toss, Add

Setting goals can be hard. This worksheet will help you think about the people, behaviors, situations, symptoms, or material things that can help you or get in the way of you reaching your goals. First, write down a goal you'd like to accomplish.

Goal: _____

Then, write down what aspects of your life you would like to keep, get rid of, and add to help you reach this goal.

Keep	Toss	Add
Good grades	Scary memories	Coping skills
Positive relationship with family	Faulty thinking	Better sleeping habits

Able versus Willing

Sometimes it can be difficult to decide between what you need to do and what you want to do. There are certain things that you may be *able* to do—like washing the dishes—but you may not be *willing* to do. There are a lot of different reasons this can happen. For example, you might be tired, want to finish playing your game, or simply find the task boring. On the following table, provide examples of times when you've been faced with a task and have been able, willing, unable, or unwilling to complete it. Some examples have been provided for you. Then, talk with a trusted adult about how you can increase your chances of feeling willing and able the next time you're faced with a task!

Able and Willing	Able and Unwilling
Getting up in the morning and going to school.	Not feeling like doing my homework.

Unable and Willing	Unable and Unwilling
Wanting to go out with my friends but feeling too sad to go.	Being asked to cook dinner, and not knowing how and not wanting to.

QUESTIONS

- What are some ways you can motivate yourself when you are able to do something but unwilling to do it?
- When are you most likely to feel able and willing to complete a task?
- What have you learned about your behaviors and choices in completing this worksheet?

My Vision, My Motivation

When the going gets tough, our motivation can keep us going! Unfortunately, it sometimes feels hard to stay motivated, which can make it difficult to get things done. While motivation drives us toward our goals, those same goals can also help get us motivated. To help you create your goals, use the vision board on the next page to draw or write what you would like to get done in the next few months or the next year. Try to think of as many things as you can that you'd like to accomplish. If that is too much, simply focus on one area where you can start. Remember, this is about you and your vision!

When you're done, think of one step you can take to work toward your vision and to shift your motivation. What things would be helpful to talk about in session to help you achieve your vision? Can you identify anything that is getting in the way of your motivation and working toward your goals?

EXPERIENTIAL USE

Create a vision board by cutting out images from magazines, drawing pictures or words, or using any other arts and crafts. Share your board with a trusted adult and discuss how you can increase your motivation to work toward your goals.

QUESTIONS

- What do you see when you look at your vision board?
- In what ways do you feel like you are already motivated and working toward your goals?
- In what ways do you feel like you are struggling or need help?

My Vision Board

Little Motivators

It can be hard to feel motivated at times, especially when you are thinking about a task that you may not like or want to complete. During these times, it can be helpful to break down that task into smaller "mini goals" and to create small rewards to help keep you motivated. Use the following chart to plan for a task or responsibility you need to complete.

My Goal:

Mini Goals:

#1	#2	#3

Steps to Take:

☐	☐	☐
☐	☐	☐
☐	☐	☐
☐	☐	☐
☐	☐	☐
☐	☐	☐

Rewards:

Time Frame:

Meet Me Where I'm At

You can't force motivation, but at the same time, it can be a challenge to find motivation. So, what can you do when there's a divide between where you are and where you want to be? When this happens, you can find the motivation to change by looking closer at what's important to *you* and what it is that *you* want to change. The more important it is to you, the more likely you'll be to work toward a change. In other words, it's totally up to YOU to decide where you want to be! Complete the following worksheet to help you identify where you are and what changes you would want to make.

One change I would like to make: _____

_____

_____

Using the following ruler, circle the number that represents how **important** this change is to you (with 0 being "not important at all" and 10 being "very important").

| 0 | 1 | 2 | 3 | 4 | 5 | 6 | 7 | 8 | 9 | 10 |

What made you choose this specific number and not a lower number?

_____

_____

_____

What would it take to move you to a higher number?

_____

_____

_____

Using the following ruler, circle the number that represents how **motivated** you are to make this change (with 0 being "not at all motivated" and 10 being "very motivated").

| 0 | 1 | 2 | 3 | 4 | 5 | 6 | 7 | 8 | 9 | 10 |

What made you choose this specific number and not a lower number?

_____

_____

_____

What would it take to move you to a higher number?

_____

_____

_____

Using the following ruler, circle the number that represents how **confident** you are that you can make this change (with 0 being "not at all confident" and 10 being "very confident").

| 0 | 1 | 2 | 3 | 4 | 5 | 6 | 7 | 8 | 9 | 10 |

What made you choose this specific number and not a lower number?

_____

_____

_____

What would it take to move you to a higher number?

_____

_____

_____

SECTION 2

Identifying and Communicating Thoughts and Feelings

The activities in the following section are primarily based in cognitive behavioral therapy (CBT), which is a modality that has proven to be effective with children and adolescents given that it is concrete and easy to understand. The first set of worksheets are focused on feelings identification. We find this incredibly powerful when working with children, as they often come into treatment not knowing how they are feeling. Sometimes we initially see kids for problems with anger, but throughout treatment, it becomes clear that they are actually struggling with depression. When children can verbalize what they are feeling and where they are feeling that emotion in their body, they are better able to manage their emotions.

The second set of worksheets are intended to help kids identify and challenge any faulty thinking patterns, or cognitive distortions, that are contributing to their distress. We have come up with creative and simple ways to teach these skills to children and adolescents. By helping children change the way they think, we can help them change the way they feel. In addition, when kids can identify their thoughts and feelings, they are better able to communicate their internal experiences with others. This skill assists in managing conflict, maintaining healthy relationships, and gaining a better understanding of themselves.

Feelings Faces

Sometimes, feelings are hard to identify and even harder to understand. For example, we may think someone is mad at us, when they are actually very worried about us! Below you will see different feeling faces. Using the word bank, find the emotion that best matches each feeling face and write it in the space provided underneath each one.

Surprised	Confused	Scared	Happy	Embarrassed	Angry
Hurt	Sad	Caring	Silly	Disgusted	Worried

_____   _____   _____   _____

_____   _____   _____   _____

_____   _____   _____   _____

EXPERIENTIAL USE

Act out each of the emotions you identified on the feeling faces!

QUESTIONS

- Was there anything hard about completing this worksheet? If so, what?
- Which emotions are harder to read on people's faces? Why?
- Do facial expression always match how a person is feeling? Why or why not?

Feelings Rainbow

Emotions are like the colors of the rainbow! There are so many different words to describe how we feel. For this worksheet, begin by coloring each section of the rainbow. You can use the classic rainbow colors (ROYGBIV) or pick your own! After you color your rainbow, think of feeling words that may be represented by that color, and write them in that line on the rainbow. For instance, you might associate blue with sadness, red with anger, and yellow with happiness. Then bring to mind a time that you experienced each emotion and share these moments with your provider or trusted adult.

EXPERIENTIAL USE

Spread different colored pieces of construction paper on the floor to represent colors of the rainbow. Walk from color to color, stopping on each to describe any feeling words represented by that color. For each color, share a time you have experienced these emotions.

You can also use this activity to think about what other people might be feeling. For example, if you had a recent argument with a friend or family member, you could stand on the colored piece of paper that you think represents how that person was feeling at the time.

Feelings Thermometer

When you have strong emotions, you can sometimes go from 0 to 100 without much warning. Other times, emotions start small and get stronger and stronger, much like the temperature rising on a thermometer. For example, anger can start off as being annoyed and then gradually increase to frustration, irritation, and then rage. For this worksheet, choose one of the seven emotion words listed at the top of the chart. Then pick five different words from that same column that you would use to describe that emotion.

Sad	Afraid	Confused	Hurt	Angry	Lonely
Depressed	Alarmed	Baffled	Crushed	Bitter	Abandoned
Empty	Distressed	Jumbled	Destroyed	Fuming	Empty
Gloomy	Frightened	Flustered	Devastated	Furious	Isolated
Hopeless	Intimidated	Shocked	Humiliated	Outraged	Neglected
Awful	Terrified	Startled	Rejected	Provoked	Rejected
Discouraged	Scared	Trapped	Defeated	Aggravated	Shamed
Miserable	Fearful	Puzzled	Criticized	Annoyed	Alone
Tearful	Nervous	Mistaken	Mistreated	Cranky	Excluded
Upset	Threatened	Misunderstood	Resentful	Irritated	Lost
Blah	Cautious	Mixed up	Used	Resentful	Detached
Disappointed	Uneasy	Uncertain	Let down	Testy	Distant
Moody	Unsure	Unsettled	Minimized	Impatient	Separate
Unhappy	Worried	Unsure	Neglected	Irked	Withdrawn

Now that you've chosen an emotion, list it above the thermometer. Use the space beside it to order, from weakest to strongest, the words from your chosen emotion column.

Emotion: _____

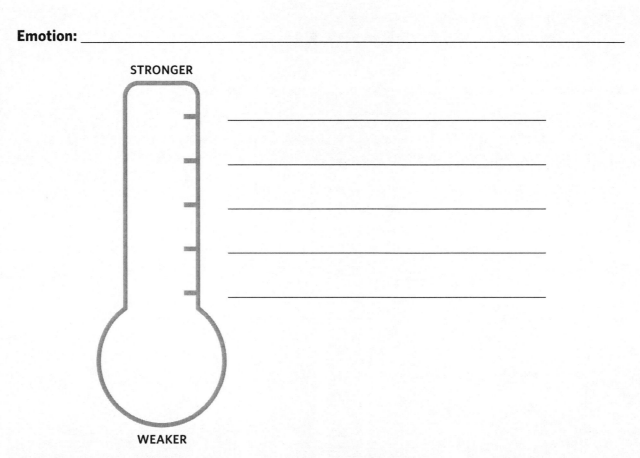

STRONGER

_____

_____

_____

_____

_____

WEAKER

Finally, think of some situations that could cause you to feel that emotion (triggers). Then describe the way your body feels when you have that emotion (body sensations). Lastly, brainstorm what you can do to feel better in situations where this emotion comes up (coping skills). Some examples have been provided for you.

Triggers	Body Sensations	Coping Skills
Being called a name	Tight fists	Walk away

Body Map

When you feel an emotion, you also experience that emotion in your body. For example, when you're nervous, you might have sweaty hands, an upset stomach, and a fast heartbeat. Being able to identify these different body signals can help you understand how you are feeling and help you talk about those feelings with others. Using the following body map, pick a color to represent each of the emotions listed on the left-hand side and mark them in the key. Then color in the parts of the body to show where you feel that emotion, and talk with a trusted adult about any situations that have made you feel that way.

Emotion Key

☐ Anger

☐ Happiness

☐ Worry

☐ Sadness

☐ Fear

☐ Guilt

Next, describe what your body might do when you experience each emotion. For example, you may have clenched fists when you feel angry.

Anger: _____

_____

Happiness: _____

_____

Worry: _____

_____

Sadness: _____

_____

Fear: _____

_____

Guilt: _____

_____

EXPERIENTIAL USE

Trace your body onto a large piece of paper. Talk with a trusted adult about the sensations you feel in your body and point to the places on the body drawing where you feel those sensations.

Brain and Body Matching Game

Sometimes your thoughts can affect the way you feel in your body! For example, if you were to think "I'm going to fail my math test," your body may react with sweaty palms or a fast heartbeat. To help you learn about the relationship between your thoughts and your body, look through the following two decks of cards. One deck is for "thoughts" and the other is for "physical sensations," meaning the feelings in your body. Cut out the cards and match the "physical sensations" cards to the "thoughts" cards that you think fit together best. Ask yourself, "When I have this thought, what might happen to my body?" There are also blank cards you can use to write and match your own thoughts or physical feelings.

Thoughts Deck

I'm going to fail.	No one likes me.	I don't fit in.	I hate my life.
Why do bad things always happen to me?	I'm going to get in trouble.	I shouldn't have done that.	I'm so angry right now.

Physical Sensations Deck

Fast heartbeat	Sweaty palms	Teary eyes	Lump in throat
Feeling like I could throw up	Tight jaw	Butterflies in stomach	Heavy breathing

Creating the Shift

Now that you've learned about how your thoughts and feelings are connected, let's learn some skills that can help you change the way your body feels—which will help change the way you think. When big emotions get in your way or are hard to control, practicing these exercises can help you have more control of your feelings and how you respond. Read through the following skills, practice them in session and on your own (again, again, and again), and then discuss with a trusted adult if needed. Remember, for these skills to be helpful during difficult times, you need to practice, practice, practice!

TIP Skills

Tip the Temperature of Your Face with Cool Water

Place a cold pack or cool rag on the area around your eyes. Breathe in deep, hold for 30 seconds, and breathe out slowly. Repeat for several minutes. You can also hold your breath as you dip your face in cold water.

Intense Exercise

Do something active to increase your heart rate for at least 20 minutes. You can jump rope, run, bike, play a sport, or get creative!

Paced Breathing

Your main focus here is to slow everything down by breathing out for longer than you breathe in. So, if you breathe in for 5 seconds, breathe out for 7 seconds. Stay focused on your breath.

Paired Muscle Relaxation

Breathe in while tightening a muscle group, hold, and then breathe out while releasing the muscle. Do this for several minutes with different muscle groups.

*See the *Head, Shoulders, Knees, and Toes* activity in section 3 for a list of all the different muscle groups!

Willingness

Use this skill to shift the feeling in your body when you are feeling angry, closed off, and shut down.

To do so, open your hands and shake them out. Then turn your palms up, with your fingers relaxed, and rest your hands on your legs (if you are seated) or by your sides (if you are standing or lying down). Take some deep, slow breaths.

Practice: Close your eyes and imagine a recent situation when you felt angry. Notice how your body starts to feel different and where your body feels tight. Now, practice willingness and notice how this skill begins to change how you feel.

*Practice in the morning or evening—or anytime you are struggling to do or accept something!

Half Smile

Use this skill to communicate to your brain that you are relaxed, calm, and accepting of the present moment.

Do this skill by relaxing your face and turning up the corners of your lips just enough that you can feel it. Other people do not necessarily have to see the smile.

Practice: Think about someone or something you dislike and notice what you feel in your body and mind. Now, practice half smiling and notice if it helps you feel more understanding and accepting.

*Practice by looking in a mirror, noticing the upturn in your lips.

Emotion Iceberg

Your behaviors can give you clues about how you are feeling. You can think of it like an iceberg: The tip of the iceberg, which floats above the surface, are the behaviors that other people can see. Below the water are the feelings that are hard for you to understand or share with others.

For example, let's say that you yell at a friend because they told someone your secret. Yelling was your behavior (the tip of the iceberg), but you probably felt a lot of different emotions underneath the surface, like anger, sadness, confusion, and hurt. Use the iceberg here to identify a behavior you've been struggling with. Underneath the water line, write down all the feelings or emotions that you have been experiencing along with or because of this behavior. Feel free to share this with a trusted adult.

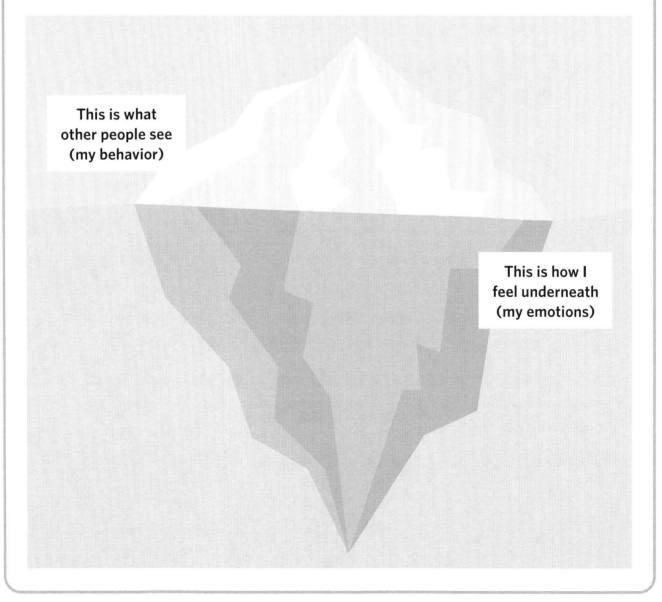

This is what other people see (my behavior)

This is how I feel underneath (my emotions)

The Power of "I"

Communicating can be tough, especially when big emotions are involved. One of the best skills to use when talking to other people about your needs is an "I feel" statement. These statements help you communicate what you need without making the other person feel like you're blaming or attacking them. Instead of using blaming language ("It's your fault" or "You hurt me"), "I feel" statements only focus on how the problem makes *you* feel. The following template shows how this statement works:

> I feel __(state your emotion)__ when you __(describe the other person's behavior)__ because __(describe how it affects you)__. What I'd like is __(describe what you want or need from the other person)__.

Use the following examples to practice changing "blaming" or "attacking" sentences to "I feel" statements.

1. You're such a jerk for telling me no!

   "I feel" statement: _____

   _____

   _____.

2. Don't yell at me.

   "I feel" statement: _____

   _____

   _____.

3. You make me so mad when you don't let me stay up late and play video games!

   "I feel" statement: _____

   _____

   _____.

4. I hate you for telling me I can't see my friends!

   "I feel" statement: _____

   _____

   _____.

5. Stop telling me what to do.

   "I feel" statement: _____

   _____

   _____.

6. If you were a good friend, you wouldn't have told my secret.

   "I feel" statement: _____

   _____

   _____.

7. You never listen to me.

   "I feel" statement: _____

   _____

   _____.

QUESTIONS

- How do you think "I feel" statements can be helpful in relationships?
- What situations in your life do you think would have been helpful to use an "I feel" statement?
- What do you think is the most difficult part of coming up with an "I feel" statement? Why?
- "I feel" statements can be used for positive emotions too! Can you think of an "I feel" statement example using a positive emotion?

Communication Styles

There are three main ways we tend to communicate with others: aggressively, assertively, and passively. Look at the table below to learn more about the three different communication styles.

	Looks like:	Sounds like:
Passive	• Shutting down and avoiding • Making poor eye contact • Not sharing your feelings or needs	• Not standing up for yourself • Saying "I'm sorry" a lot • Saying "It's okay" when it's not okay • Saying "I'm fine" when you're not

Aggressive	• Yelling, being hurtful, and using blaming language
	• Not letting others talk
	• Finger pointing, rolling your eyes, and getting in someone's personal space
		• Using "you" statements, like:
		  – "You were the one who chose that restaurant."
		  – "Why didn't you listen to me?"
		  – "You were wrong."
		  – "You better let me have my phone back, or I'm going to run away."

Assertive	• Making good eye contact
	• Being calm and confident
	• Respecting yourself while respecting others too
	• Being honest
	• Listening
		• Making a request or stating your needs, like:
		  – "It hurt my feelings when you didn't text me back the other night."
		  – "I don't want pizza tonight. Can we have tacos instead?"
		  – "Can I wear sneakers instead of sandals?"

Identifying Communication Styles

There are several styles of communication. Let's practice identifying between the different styles. Read the following sentences and circle whether each is an example of aggressive, passive, or assertive communication.

1. Your mom tells you that you need to finish your homework before watching TV, and you tell her "I don't need to listen to you!"

   Aggressive   **Passive**   **Assertive**

2. Last Tuesday, your friend told one of your secrets to everyone in your class. Your feelings are hurt, but you haven't talked to her about it.

   Aggressive   **Passive**   **Assertive**

3. You're late to practice—again! You call your coach on the way and take responsibility for being late.

   Aggressive   **Passive**   **Assertive**

4. Your sister borrowed your shirt without asking your permission. When you talk to her about it, you say "You're always taking my stuff! You're such a brat!"

   Aggressive   **Passive**   **Assertive**

5. You and your friend agree to sit next to each other on the bus for the field trip. Another friend asks if you will sit with her instead. You tell her that you would like to, but you've already agreed to sit with your other friend.

   Aggressive   **Passive**   **Assertive**

6. You really want to sign up for soccer, but your friend wants you to join the drama club with him instead. You end up joining the drama club because you don't want to let your friend down or hurt his feelings.

   Aggressive   **Passive**   **Assertive**

Act It Out

We don't just communicate with our words (*verbal communication*), we also communicate with our facial expressions, eye contact, and body language (*nonverbal communication*). Did you know that nonverbal behaviors make up over 90 percent of all communication? That means they're pretty important! This activity will help you understand your nonverbal behaviors and give you an opportunity to practice your nonverbal communication skills with a trusted adult. To do so, act out the emotions listed below without using any words. Don't let your partner know which feeling you are acting out—the goal is to make them guess based only on your nonverbal cues! As you act out the emotions, make sure to use your body language and facial expressions so your partner can guess which emotion you are acting out.

1. Shy/nervous

2. Happy/confident

3. Uninterested/bored

4. You pick!

After acting out each emotion, ask your partner the following questions:

- What emotion was I feeling?

- What did I do to show that emotion?

- What did my body look like?

Roadblocks

It can be hard to express yourself to others. Sometimes you get stuck—because you are worried, you have a hard time trusting others, or you are having really big emotions—and it feels like you're hitting a roadblock. What makes it hard for you to communicate your wants and needs? Read the following roadblocks and check off any that are true for you.

☐ What will other people say?

☐ I'm so overwhelmed, I can't think.

☐ What if they don't like me anymore?

☐ Will they understand?

☐ No one listens.

☐ Who cares, right?

☐ It doesn't matter.

☐ I'm so angry right now!

☐ Why is this happening to me?

☐ This isn't going to work anyway.

☐ They'll just disappoint and hurt me too.

☐ I just want everyone to be happy and no one to be angry.

☐ They're not going to get it.

☐ What will they think?

☐ What will they say?

☐ It looks so easy for them.

Tricky Thoughts

Tricky thoughts, or cognitive distortions, can be described as the little negative voice in your head that puts you down, makes you feel bad, or clouds your thinking. The following list includes some of the most common tricky thoughts. Put a check mark by any that you struggle with.

☐ **Ignoring the Good**

You pay attention when bad things happen and ignore times when something good happens. For example, you get one answer wrong on a test, and all you can think about is your mistake instead of all the other answers you got right.

☐ **All-or-Nothing Thinking**

You believe things are either right or wrong, good or bad. For example, "If I can't be perfect, then there is no point in trying."

☐ **Overgeneralization**

When something bad happens just once, you think it will happen again and again. For example, you get a bad grade on a test and think that you will fail every test from now on and get held back.

☐ **Jumping to Conclusions**

○ **Mind Reading**

You think you know what other people are thinking and feeling. For example, your friend doesn't text you back as quickly as she usually does, so you think, "She must be mad at me."

○ **Fortune Telling**

You make predictions, without evidence, that bad things will happen in the future. For example, you leave a voicemail for your friend and think, "I know they aren't going to call me back."

☐ **Minimizing/Magnifying**

You tend to make a big deal out of something small (magnifying) or claim that something is "not a big deal" even though it might be (minimizing). For example, you think your life is awful because your parents won't let you stay the night with a friend on a Friday (magnifying). Or you believe that it "wasn't a big deal" that you won the school spelling bee (minimizing).

☐ **Personalization**

You take everything personally, even if it doesn't have anything to do with you. For example, when walking by a group of peers in the hallway at school, you think, "They must be talking about me."

☐ **Blaming**

You hold other people responsible for how you feel, for your behaviors, or for the outcome of a situation. For example, "It's the teacher's fault I failed the test because she didn't teach me well enough."

☐ **Should've, Could've, Would've**

You believe things have to be a certain way, or you focus on the past or things you can't change. For example, you think that people *should* always be nice to you.

☐ **Feelings as Facts**

You believe that if you feel something, then it must be true. For example, "I feel like a loser, so I must be a loser."

Identifying Tricky Thoughts

Now that you've learned a little about what tricky thoughts are, let's see if you can identify them in some common examples. Match each tricky thought in the left-hand column with the correct example in the right-hand column. When you're finished, talk with a trusted adult about a time when you experienced each type of tricky thought.

1. Overgeneralization

2. Blaming

3. Should've, Could've, Would've

4. Personalization

5. Magnifying/Minimizing

6. Ignoring the Good

7. Jumping to Conclusions (Mind Reading)

8. Jumping to Conclusions (Fortune Telling)

9. Feelings as Facts

10. All-or-Nothing Thinking

A. "Since I can't clean my whole room right now, I'm not doing it at all."

B. "I feel scared, so I must be in danger."

C. "Why do the worst things always happen to me? It's always my fault."

D. **Parent:** "Next time try a bit harder on your test."
You: "My parents think I'm an idiot and a failure."

E. "If I would've listened to my dad, I wouldn't be in trouble for lying."

F. "I stuttered during my class presentation, so I'll never be good at speaking in public."

G. "Because I missed one question on my final, I might as well have failed it."

H. "It's all your fault that I feel bad about myself."

I. "I only got a 94 on my test."

J. "I just know I'm not going to make any friends at my new school."

Answer Key: 1.F 2.H 3.E 4.C 5.G 6.I 7.D 8.J 9.B 10.A

Balancing All-or-Nothing Thinking

This worksheet will teach you the skill of balanced thinking by helping you see different points of view. All-or-nothing thinking can make you believe that things are either right or wrong, good or bad—with nothing in between—but the reality is that there is a gray area in most situations. To help you find this gray area, use the seesaw below to balance out your thinking. Think about a recent situation where you had all-or-nothing thinking. On each side of the seesaw, write down your all-or-nothing thoughts. Then use the middle of the seesaw to write down a more balanced way of thinking.

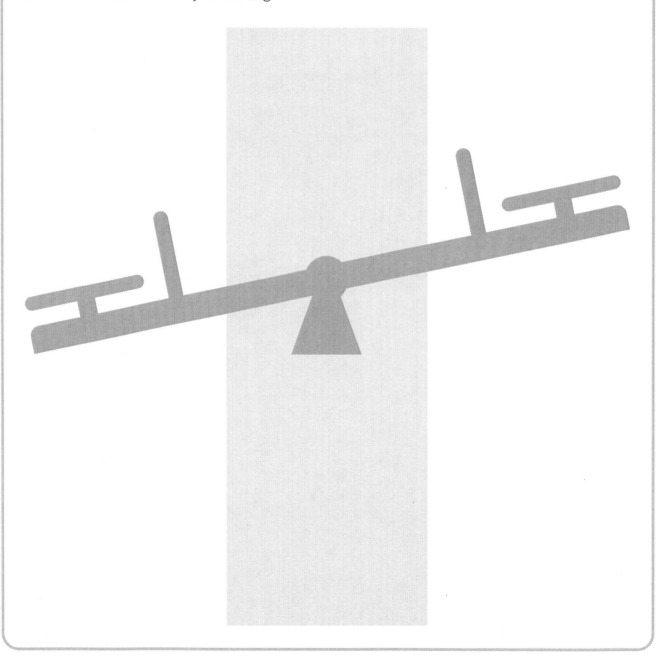

Overgeneralization

One of the most common thinking errors is overgeneralization, which happens when you draw broad conclusions based on one or more experiences. For example, if you have a rough start to your morning on a Monday, you may think "All Mondays are *horrible*," even though you may have had some Mondays that went well in the past. Below are some common overgeneralizing statements. Try rewriting each statement to create a more factual thought.

1. You lose your last soccer game of the season and think, "My team *always* loses our games."

   Factual thought: _____

   _____.

2. Your mom doesn't let you order pizza for dinner, so you think, "I *never* get to choose what we have for dinner."

   Factual thought: _____

   _____.

3. You get into a fight with one of your peers and think, "*All* the kids in my class hate me."

   Factual thought: _____

   _____.

4. You overhear another kid talking about you and think, "*Everybody* is talking about me."

   Factual thought: _____

   _____.

5. Your parents are busy working and tell you they don't have time right now to hear your thoughts about the upcoming family vacation. You think, "*Nobody* cares what I think."

   Factual thought: _____

   _____.

Ages 12+

Jumping to Conclusions
(Mind Reading or Fortune Telling)

When you jump to conclusions, you assume you know what other people are thinking or feeling (mind reading) or you believe things will turn out badly (fortune telling), even when there are no facts to support our beliefs. While jumping to conclusions can seem quick and simple, it can also cause a lot of problems because your conclusions aren't always right. To help you challenge this type of thinking, read the facts in the left column and write the first thought that pops in your head in the right-most column (conclusion), even if it sounds silly. Then write an alternative conclusion or other possible thought in the middle column (alternatives).

Let's Jump!

Facts	Alternatives	Conclusion
You text someone that you are interested in talking to and they leave you on "read."		
You walk into a room and two people you are not friends with look your direction and start giggling and whispering.		

Facts	Alternatives	Conclusion
You see a man and woman run out of a store to their car and speed away.		
Your parent/guardian texts you and says, "We need to talk."		
You notice that one of your friends is no longer following you on social media.		

Dealing with Impulsivity and Distractibility

"Why is she doing that?"

"They are always late!"

"Stop! That's not safe!"

"Pay attention!"

These are all phrases you may have heard people say (or even said yourself) to kids who experience executive functioning challenges. Executive functioning skills are a part of what helps our brains stay organized, get things done, and make safe, helpful decisions. These skills include time management, focus, planning, organization, flexible thinking, working memory, and self-control. When these skills are lacking, kids can exhibit challenges with behavior, such as impulsivity (i.e., acting without thinking) and distractibility (i.e., difficulty paying attention).

Therefore, this section includes several tools to help you teach and assess executive functioning skills, as well as tangible activities that will help kids learn and develop these skills. Each activity was created with *neurodiversity* in mind—the idea that everyone's brain works differently! These activities will help developing brains learn how to stop and think before acting, so kids can make better choices. Whether you're trying to help your client improve their ability to focus, learn how to organize busy schedules, or have better control over their extra busy bodies, the activities in this section provide easy, hands-on tools to bolster these important life skills.

Organized Brain

Executive functioning skills allow your brain to stay organized, get stuff done, and make safe and helpful decisions. These include skills like time management, focus, planning, organization, flexible thinking, working memory, and self-control. On the following rating scales, give yourself a score for each of the executive functioning skills (with 0 being "least skillful" and 5 being "most skillful"). Then, circle any of the suggestions that you think may help you to improve that skill or write in your own.

Time management: Knowing how long it will take to complete a task and using your time well

0	1	2	3	4	5

You can try:

Creating a routine or schedule   Starting things early

Setting a timer   Giving yourself breaks

Other: _____

Focus: Being able to pay attention to the activity you are doing and staying on task

0	1	2	3	4	5

You can try:

Doing one thing at a time   Going to a quiet place

Belly breathing   Using a fidget toy

Listening to music   Breaking down tasks into smaller parts

Other: _____

Planning: Creating goals, deciding how you are going to reach them, and thinking ahead

0	1	2	3	4	5

You can try: Keeping a planner   Using a calendar   Writing lists

Setting small, short-term deadlines   Ordering your to-do list from most important to least important

Other: _____

Organization: Keeping things orderly, having or creating a system that works

0	1	2	3	4	5

You can try: Creating small tasks   Color-coding   Having a daily routine

Creating memory aids (e.g., flashcards)   Organizing your study space

Using organization tools (e.g., binders with tabs, planners, visual aids)

Other: _____

Flexible thinking: Thinking outside of the box to solve problems, being open to new ideas

0	1	2	3	4	5

You can try: Making up new rules for games   Coming up with new jokes

Doing puzzles   Asking others their opinions   Coming up with a plan B

Finding more than one way to do everyday things (e.g., making a sandwich in a different order, putting on your pants with the leg you don't usually start with)

Other: _____

Working memory: Being able to remember information in the short term (e.g., keeping your place on a page while reading, remembering instructions as you are trying to get something done)

| 0 | 1 | 2 | 3 | 4 | 5 |

You can try: Playing matching games   Creating rhymes or songs

Drawing what you need to get done   Breaking things into smaller tasks

Using visual reminders (e.g., checklists, calendars)

Other: _____

Self-Control: Being able to think before you act

| 0 | 1 | 2 | 3 | 4 | 5 |

You can try: Using deep breathing   Talking about your feelings

Creating a routine   Counting to 10 before making a decision

Creating a calm-down space

Other: _____

Primary...Secondary

Sometimes when we have an urge to do something, we act on the first thought that pops into our head. This can also happen when we feel a big emotion, especially if that feeling is unexpected. This worksheet will help you think about what your first, or primary, thought is and then what your next, or secondary, thought is in different situations. Usually, pausing and listening to that secondary thought can help you slow down and think about the possible consequences of acting on an urge or emotion. Fill in the blanks for each situation with both your primary and secondary thoughts. An example has been provided for you first.

The teacher asks a question that you know the answer to.

Primary thought: I want to say the answer.

Secondary thought: I need to raise my hand and wait to be called on.

You find out that a friend is talking about you behind your back.

Primary thought: _____

Secondary thought: _____

Your parent or guardian asks you to do something you don't want to do.

Primary thought: _____

Secondary thought: _____

You see something posted about you on social media that isn't true.

Primary thought: _____

Secondary thought: _____

You aren't picked to be on the sports team you tried out for.

Primary thought: _____

Secondary thought: _____

As a consequence, your parents take away your cell phone for a week.

Primary thought: _____

Secondary thought: _____

Your video game character is killed by another player.

Primary thought: _____

Secondary thought: _____

You walk into the classroom and see a group of kids whispering.

Primary thought: _____

Secondary thought: _____

A friend makes fun of you.

Primary thought: _____

Secondary thought: _____

First, Second, Last

Sometimes you need to do tasks that are made up of a lot of different, smaller steps. It can be tough to decide in what order to perform these smaller steps. The steps can feel all tangled in your brain, which may make you feel frustrated, confused, or overwhelmed. This worksheet will help you practice how to plan and *prioritize* steps, which means putting them in an order that makes the most sense. Read the following examples and identify the steps needed to complete the tasks. Then talk to a trusted adult to review the plan and add any steps you might have missed.

1. Aiden just woke up and has to get ready for school.

   - _____
   - _____
   - _____
   - _____
   - _____

2. Luca wants to invite a friend over to play.

   - _____
   - _____
   - _____
   - _____

3. Ariella would like to make a peanut butter and jelly sandwich for lunch.

   - _____
   - _____
   - _____
   - _____
   - _____

4. Ray has to get ready for his football game.

    - _____
    - _____
    - _____
    - _____
    - _____

5. Ava would like to make a list of all the assignments she has to finish by the end of the week.

    - _____
    - _____
    - _____
    - _____
    - _____

6. Opie's chore for tonight is to clean the kitchen.

    - _____
    - _____
    - _____
    - _____
    - _____

Make it Memorable

Sometimes remembering tasks, lists, or the order of things can be hard! One way to make your memory stronger is to use a learning technique called a mnemonic device. To create a mnemonic device, you simply take the first letter of each word that you need to remember and develop a catchy saying based on those letters. For this worksheet, think of something you have a hard time remembering and write it in the thought bubble. Then create a mnemonic device to go with it in the space beside it. An example has been provided for you first.

Mnemonic Device

<u>M</u>ercury, <u>V</u>enus, <u>E</u>arth, <u>M</u>ars, <u>J</u>upiter, <u>S</u>aturn, <u>U</u>ranus, <u>N</u>eptune, <u>P</u>luto

<u>M</u>y <u>V</u>ery <u>E</u>xcellent <u>M</u>other <u>J</u>ust <u>S</u>erved <u>U</u>s <u>N</u>ine <u>P</u>izzas

Mnemonic Device

Tic Toc Timer

Time management skills include being on time and knowing how long it will take you to finish a task. These skills are important for many different areas of life, including when you're at school, playing on a sports team, or simply getting ready in the morning to start your day. One way to improve your time management skills is to guess how long it will take you to complete tasks and then use a timer to see how long it actually takes. Let's try it out!

Task	Your Guess	Actual Time
Jump up and down 50 times		
Look up the world record for the fastest mile		
Write a word for each letter of the alphabet		
Drink a glass of water		
Make your bed		
Check your social media updates		
Wash the dishes		
Go for a walk around the block		
Order a pizza		
Do your homework		
Take a bath or shower		
Other:		

QUESTIONS

- What did you notice about the time it actually took you to do each of these tasks compared to your guesses?
- In what situations do you think you need the most help with time management skills?
- Is there anyone who can help you with time management? Who?

Stoplight

It can be tough when you don't want to do something. You might become frustrated—or even angry—and act out in not-so-great ways. Use the stoplight on the next page to talk about your behaviors at school. The red light represents behaviors or actions that will get you into trouble or are against the rules. The yellow light represents behaviors or actions that you may get a warning for. The green light represents behaviors or actions that are positive and that someone at school would praise you for (e.g., being kind to your classmates, getting good grades). Next to each light color, write down the different behaviors or actions you have at school.

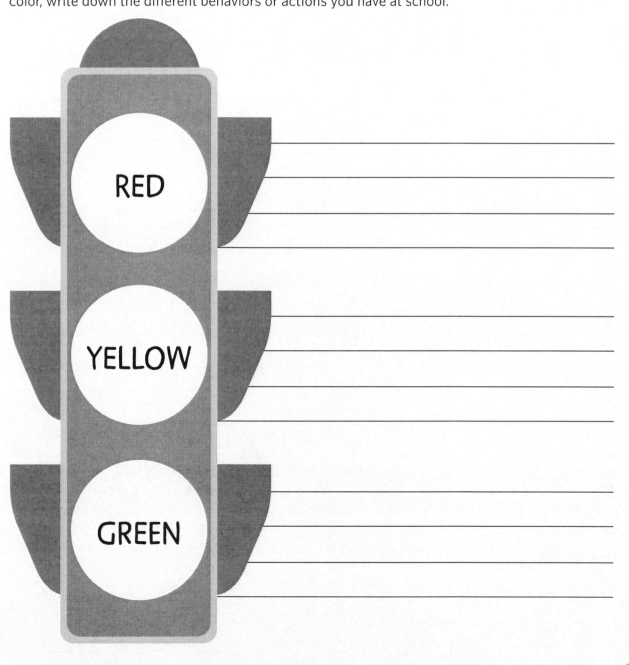

RED

YELLOW

GREEN

EXPERIENTIAL USE #1:

This activity can be modified for a classroom environment by having the counselor or teacher first complete the previous stoplight exercise with the student to identify red, yellow, and green behaviors. With the student's feedback, the teacher can then develop a creative, nonverbal accountability system to indicate when the student is engaging in these behaviors. For instance, the teacher might put a red, yellow, or green card on the student's desk or on the board as a reminder to check in with their current behavior.

EXPERIENTIAL USE #2:

The teacher can create a "racetrack" inside the classroom. When the teacher notices and calls out a behavior, the student will decide the category in which the behavior belongs (e.g., red, yellow, or green) and respond accordingly (e.g., standing still, walking slowly, walking fast, respectively).

What's Underneath?

Sometimes it can be hard to focus. Though you can't always give every task your full attention, it is helpful to be aware of the distractions that make it difficult to stay on track. This worksheet will help you look at things that get in the way of finishing your schoolwork and chores. Look at the following list and place a check mark by each item that makes it hard to focus. You can also use the blank spaces to come up with some of your own!

☐ Noticing your mind wandering

☐ Scrolling through social media or your phone (e.g., getting distracted by posts, updates, messages)

☐ Watching too much TV

☐ Watching or creating videos

☐ Playing games

☐ Feeling uncomfortable physical symptoms (e.g., heart racing, shaking, stomachache)

☐ Being in pain (physical or emotional)

☐ Hearing too much noise (e.g., when things are too loud or distracting)

☐ Wanting to hang out with friends

☐ Going to sports practice or other extracurricular activities

☐ Feeling certain emotions (e.g., frustration, boredom, impatience)

☐ Feeling too much pressure (e.g., grades, future, expectations)

☐ Having a busy body (e.g., too many things to do and get done)

☐ Other: _____

☐ Other: _____

How Do You Stay Organized?

Organization is a tough skill to teach, as everyone seems to have their own way of staying organized. But being *unorganized* can cause confusion, trigger frustration, and make you not care. Complete the table below with a trusted adult to talk about what organizational skills may work best for you! For each organizational idea, write down all the ways it could help in the "pros" column and all the ways it could be difficult or unhelpful in the "cons" column. An example has been provided for you first.

Organizational Idea	Pros	Cons
Create several smaller tasks (e.g., instead of cleaning the whole kitchen, make a list of each task, such as unloading the dishwasher)	I don't become overwhelmed.	It takes more time.
Use a color-coding system		
Create memory aids (e.g., flashcards)		

Organizational Idea	Pros	Cons
Use an electronic or written planner		
Make to-do lists		
Use a white board		
Use notebooks or a binder with tabs to organize subjects (e.g., math, reading, science)		

Empowering Parents

When your child starts school, you may not know what to ask, you might be fearful of judgment, or it could be difficult to understand the information presented to you. Use the following checklist to ensure you have all the information you need for your child's schooling.

☐ **Assigned teacher's information (name, phone number, email address):** Does the teacher use an app to communicate or send updates? How often do they update grades? Where can you find information on grades? How will you know if your child is struggling? How do they prefer that you communicate your needs and concerns?

☐ **School counselor or school social worker's information (name, phone number, email address):** What is their role within the context of the school system? What services do they provide to the school, the children, and the children's families?

☐ **Classroom expectations:** What are the expectations of the classroom as a whole? How is conflict handled? Is there any flexibility in the expectations? What happens when there are issues between students? What is the message surrounding expectations that can be implemented at home?

☐ **Additional services or accommodations (if necessary):** What additional services are offered at the school? Who is the main contact for these services (and what is their contact information)? What are the "rules" (e.g., state or local laws) on obtaining these services? What documentation do you need? How can you ensure your voice is heard?

☐ **Involvement:** What opportunities are there for parental involvement within the school? Are there any rules or guidelines you should be aware of? Can you volunteer in your child's classroom? What does the school allow for celebrations (e.g., birthdays, holidays)?

☐ **Sports, music, art, and clubs:** What extracurricular activities are offered? If something is not offered at school, are there outside recommendations? What if you can't afford the cost associated with elective activities?

☐ **Policies and procedures:** Is make-up work allowed? How are students expected to ask for help—academically, behaviorally, socially, emotionally? What are the guidelines surrounding suspension or expulsion? Whom do you contact for issues with your child's teacher?

☐ **Emergencies:** How is an emergency defined? How are emergencies handled? How does the school communicate with parents during an emergency? When does the school call for outside help during an emergency? Is there a backup plan in these instances? How can you ensure your child's safety?

Bubbles

Mindfulness is all about slowing down and focusing your attention on what you're doing right here, right now. When you practice mindfulness, you notice what is going on around you by using your five senses: sight, sound, smell, taste, and touch. In this activity, you'll practice using your five senses as you blow bubbles. So, grab some bubbles and follow the prompts to practice your mindfulness skills!

Look at the <u>shape</u> of the bubble . . . watch it change as it floats through the air.

Name all of the different <u>colors</u> you see in the bubbles.

Try to catch a bubble in your hand, and describe how it <u>feels</u>.

See if you can <u>count</u> how many bubbles are floating in front of you at one time.

Pop a bubble and <u>listen</u> for the sound it makes.

Head, Shoulders, Knees, and Toes

When it is difficult for your body to calm down, it can make you feel physically uncomfortable (e.g., butterflies in your stomach) and affect the way you think and feel (e.g., make you feel nervous). This activity will use the song "Head, Shoulders, Knees, and Toes" to teach you how to use all your muscles to keep your body calm. Have a trusted adult read the following script so you can follow along.

1. Before we start, rate how tight your body is feeling right now on a scale of 1 to 10 (with 1 being "super tight" and 10 being "totally relaxed").

2. Then start at your head and, using the muscles in your forehead, scrunch your eyebrows. Hold for three seconds and release. Take a deep breath in through your nose for four seconds, and then out through your mouth for four seconds.

3. Next, bring your attention to your eyes. Close your eyes as tightly as you can and hold for three seconds, then release. Again, take a deep breath in through your nose for four seconds, and then out through your mouth for four seconds.

4. Notice your cheeks and jaw. Smile and frown to see where these muscles are in your face. Now smile as BIG as you can—holding it for three seconds—and then let your smile go.

5. Next, move to your shoulders and neck. See if you can raise your shoulders up and try to touch your ears with them without moving your head. Breathe in and hold your shoulders up for four seconds, and then breathe out as you drop them down.

6. Now give yourself a big hug and feel the tops of your arms. Then drop your arms and make fists with your hands, squeezing as hard as you can. Squeeze for four seconds, then let go, relaxing your arms and dropping them down to your side. Shake out your hands and roll your wrists, noticing the energy leave that part of your body. Take a deep breath in through your nose, then out through your mouth.

7. Next focus on your chest—the spot a necklace would hang if you were wearing one. Put your arms behind your back, bringing your shoulder blades in toward one another while trying to touch your elbows behind your back. Hold this position and breathe in for four seconds, then exhale for four seconds and bring your shoulders and chest back to resting position. Let go of any tightness in your chest.

8. Now put your hands over your belly, near your belly button. Squeeze all the muscles in your belly as hard as you can. Then let your muscles relax and take a big belly breath in for four seconds, watching your belly inflate like a balloon as you breathe in. Exhale for four seconds, letting all the air out and watching your belly drop back down.

9. Next, bring your attention to the muscles in your thighs. These are a huge group of muscles! See if you can squeeze all these muscles, making them as tight as you can. Hold those muscles tight for four seconds, then release. See how much you can relax them and how it feels different from when you had them tightened.

10. Move down to your calves, and see how hard you can make these muscles in the backs of your legs. Try standing on your tiptoes. Next, try flexing both your feet, pointing your toes, to see how tight your calf muscles become. Squeeze those muscles and hold for four seconds, then release. Take your hands and shake your calves, noticing how soft they have become.

11. Now notice your feet and toes. Try scrunching your toes as hard as you can and hold for four seconds, then release.

12. Last, shake out your whole body to release any remaining tightness in your muscles. Take one last deep breath, then breathe out through your mouth.

QUESTIONS

- What do you notice is different about your body now that we have done our relaxation activity?
- Are you feeling any different? In what ways?
- On a scale of 1–10, using the same scale from the beginning, how tight does your body feel now?

Choices

When you make one choice, you are also making several *other* choices that you may not be thinking about in the moment. That's why it's important to learn how to think ahead! Although this can be a tough skill to learn, it gives you a lot more control over your choices. To help you practice this skill, look at the choice listed in the first section of each arrow. In the spaces to the right, write down any other choices that may come along with making the first choice. An example has been provided for you first.

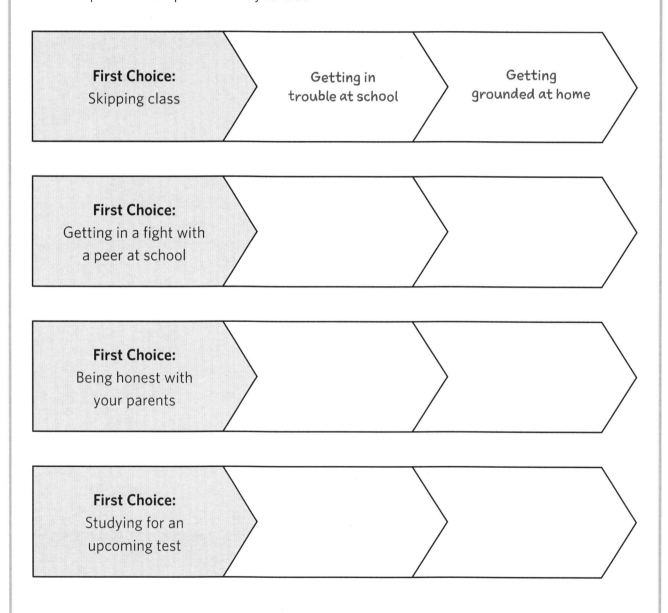

First Choice:
Skipping class

Getting in trouble at school

Getting grounded at home

First Choice:
Getting in a fight with a peer at school

First Choice:
Being honest with your parents

First Choice:
Studying for an upcoming test

First Choice:
Lying to your coach

First Choice:
Not completing
your chores

First Choice:
Not turning in your
assignments

First Choice:

First Choice:

First Choice:

If . . . Then

Thinking about consequences *before* you decide to do something is an important skill that can keep you out of trouble and support healthy, trusting relationships. Read through the following list and complete the sentences with what you believe may happen in these scenarios.

If I don't complete my schoolwork, then _____

_____.

If I make a mistake, then _____

_____.

If I lie to my family, then _____

_____.

If I am mean to my friends, then _____

_____.

If I don't follow the rules, then _____

_____.

If I lose my temper, then _____

_____.

If I ask for help, then _____

_____.

If I apologize, then _____

_____.

If I talk about how I feel, then _____

_____.

Managing Difficult Feelings and Behaviors

When your client struggles with anger, self-injury, or other self-sabotaging behaviors, you can't really work on anything else until they are able to make safe choices. To manage these difficult feelings and behaviors, you have to understand *why* kids are making these choices so you can then work on developing new behaviors that still allow them to get their needs met. No one wakes up angry or wanting to hurt themselves. Typically, kids are triggered by something in their environment, and these triggers build until they cause an explosion of behaviors. Whether these behaviors are external (e.g., hitting, throwing things, risky sexual activity) or internal (e.g., cutting, binging/restricting), they are still unsafe. Therefore, we've included several tools in this section that allow you to dive deeper and get to the root of the problem.

Addressing these concerns can be compared to putting pieces of a puzzle together. Your client is one piece, you (as the treatment provider) are another piece, and families are another—and they work most effectively when they share a common understanding. When you work with children or adolescents, you are also working with their parents, caregivers, and often other members of the client's family, so this section also includes family worksheets that assist in creating structure and safety within the home and the parent-child relationship. These tools are designed to start the conversation and ensure all parties are on the same page.

Our Anger

Anger looks different for everyone, and there are so many things that can make people feel angry. Sometimes it can be difficult to figure out how to control your anger without knowing your triggers. Complete the following sentences with a trusted adult to better understand what makes you angry and how you think and behave when you are angry.

1. One thing that makes me angry is _____.

2. When I am angry, I _____.

3. Three things I notice in my body when I'm angry are _____,

   _____, and _____.

4. When I'm angry, I don't want _____.

5. When I'm angry, I need _____.

6. Someone who can help when I'm angry is _____.

7. One thing that helps when I'm angry is _____.

8. One unhealthy way I express anger is _____.

9. One healthy way I express anger is _____.

10. A thought I have when I feel angry is _____.

11. Some consequences I've had because of my anger are _____.

12. When I'm angry, people think _____.

13. My anger makes me feel _____ about myself.

14. Something that makes me feel a little bit angry is _____.

15. The first thing that happens when I start to feel angry is _____.

16. The worst thing about my anger is _____.

17. I get angry when I feel _____.

Ages
8+

Layers of Anger

For some people, anger can come on quickly and feel like an explosion! For other people, anger can start small and build slowly until they finally explode. There are also different types and levels of anger. For example, some things might make you feel annoyed, while others might fill you with rage.

You can think of anger like a cake with many layers. To help you understand these layers, use the word bank to fill in the cake with different words that represent anger. Fill the bottom layer of the cake with emotions that represent the least intense anger and the upper layers with emotions that are associated with the biggest anger. When you are done, use the space on the candles to write down some behaviors you have when you are super angry.

When you're done filling in the cake, blow out the candles! Take a deep breath in and slowly pretend to blow out each candle. Picture yourself with the ability to control your anger and behavior.

my emotions when I'm the most angry:

my emotions when I'm even more angry:

Irritated	Grumpy
Furious	Frustrated
Annoyed	Angry
Enraged	Upset
Mad	Infuriated
Upset	Grouchy
Livid	Unhappy
Agitated	Aggravated

my emotions when I'm more angry:

my emotions when I'm a little angry:

Ages 8+

Don't Break the Ice

Anger can be just like ice. When ice is frozen solid, it's difficult to break, but with enough pressure, it can crack. This is when your anger can get the best of you. Knowing what triggers your anger can be helpful to control your reactions *before* they get you in trouble. On each of the following blocks of ice, write or draw something that make you angry—these are your anger triggers. For each trigger, rate how upsetting the trigger is for you on a scale of 1 to 5 (with 1 being "not very upsetting" and 5 being "the most upsetting"). The more upsetting the trigger, the more likely it is that your ice will break!

Trigger: _____

Rating (1-5): _____

Trigger: _____

Rating (1-5): _____

Trigger: _____

Rating (1-5): _____

Trigger: _____

Rating (1-5): _____

QUESTIONS

- How might it be helpful to share your triggers with those you care about?
- What are some warning signs that your ice is about to break?
- What are some things that could make your triggers feel smaller?

Ages
10+

Anger Earthquake

Earthquakes can happen unexpectedly and leave behind a lot of damage. And just like earthquakes, an angry reaction to a problem could lead to negative consequences for yourself and your relationships. Think about what happens in your life after you have an angry outburst. Imagine that the following earthquake represents your anger. Write or draw all the possible consequences, or "damage," that your anger can cause.

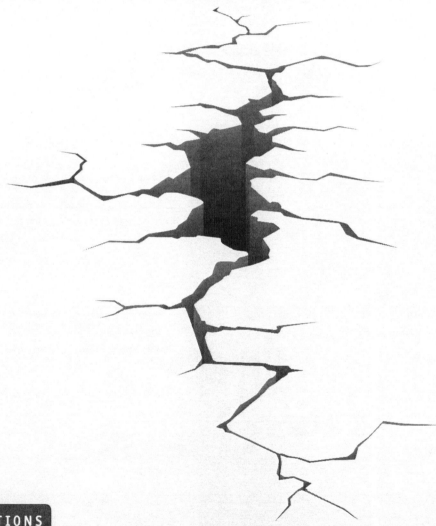

QUESTIONS

- What happens when you get angry? Does it happen quickly, or can you see it coming?
- How can you repair the damage of your anger earthquake?
- How can you prevent the anger earthquake from happening?
- What skills do you have to control your anger in the moment? Do you think you need more skills?

Your Anger Volcano

Although anger is one emotion, it is often made up of many different parts, including other emotions, body sensations, situations, and worries. By exploring these parts, you can understand not only how your anger is created and develops, but how to better control it when you feel an eruption beginning to happen. Use the following volcano to identify as many parts of your anger as possible. Next, refer to the *Ways to Manage Anger* activity on the next page to learn effective ways to keep your anger volcano from erupting.

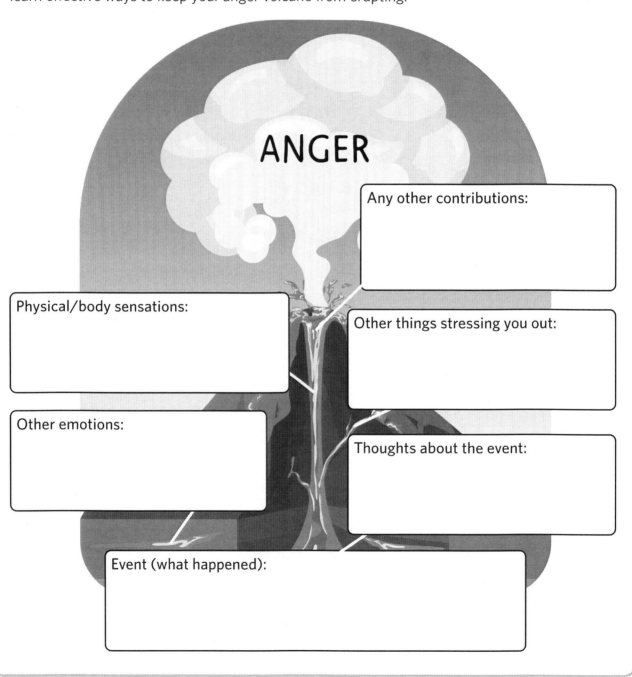

ANGER

Any other contributions:

Physical/body sensations:

Other things stressing you out:

Other emotions:

Thoughts about the event:

Event (what happened):

Ways to Manage Anger

When you feel like your anger volcano might explode, there are several strategies you can use to cool down and keep the lava from erupting. Using the following list, pick some activities you think could be helpful to improve your anger in those moments. Discuss with your treatment provider or a trusted adult.

☐ **Focus on your breath:** No matter where you are, focusing on your breath can be helpful in bringing down strong emotions and allowing you to think more clearly. Make sure to take deep breaths in and breathe all your air out.

☐ **Distract your mind:** Find something to briefly distract your mind and calm you down. For example, you could talk to a friend, go for a walk, play a game, or listen to a song.

☐ **Focus on your five senses:** List out as many things as you can see, hear, smell, taste, and touch around you.

☐ **Slow everything down:** Close your eyes and cover them with a cold rag, or gently put your face into some cold water. Remember, whatever you use, it doesn't have to be freezing—just cold!

☐ **Do progressive muscle relaxation:** Practice tensing and relaxing your muscles to release some of the tension that anger causes (see the *Head, Shoulders, Knees, and Toes* activity in section 3 for a step-by-step tutorial on muscle relaxation).

☐ **Other:** _____

_____

_____

Rule Setting

While setting rules for your household may seem like an easy task, it is not the same as simply creating a long list of your child's negative behaviors and what they can do to fix them. You need to consider what is most important for all the members of your family—and make these top priorities clear and well-defined for everyone. Rules can sometimes be confusing, especially when they are miscommunicated. This worksheet will help you work with your child to identify top problem areas and create rules in your family.

Parents:

- What are your biggest concerns regarding your child's negative behaviors?

  _____

  _____

- Are there any concerns you can let go of or change the expectations for?

  _____

  _____

- What are the current consequences and rewards?

  _____

  _____

Child:

- What rules would you identify as "fair"?

  _____

  _____

- What rules would you identify as "unfair"?

  _____

  _____

- What would you like to see as rewards and consequences?

  _____

  _____

Now, work together to identify the two biggest concerns to focus on. These concerns should have the biggest impact on important life areas, such as safety, school, chores, and work. Use the following boxes on the next page to write clear expectations and consequences for these two concerns. Then grade how well you're currently doing managing each concern. This information can be used in future sessions to help create goals and identify barriers to improve the concerns.

Concern #1: _____

Expectation: _____

Consequence: _____

Parent Grade (0-100%): _____

Child Grade (0-100%): _____

Agreed-Upon Grade (0-100%): _____

Concern #2: _____

Expectation: _____

Consequence: _____

Parent Grade (0-100%): _____

Child Grade (0-100%): _____

Agreed-Upon Grade (0-100%): _____

Family Contract

Family contracts are a great tool to clarify expectations, allow everyone to have a voice, facilitate communication about what is and is not working, and help each family member take accountability. The following is an example of a contract. Feel free to use the contract as is, make small changes, or create your own based on the needs of your family.

The _____ **Family Contract**

Family Goal: _____

Top Three Identified Problems:

1. _____
2. _____
3. _____

Expectations:

1. *School*

    a. Wake up daily (without parental reminders) at _____ for school to start at _____.

    b. Brush your teeth, wash your face, and ensure you are presentable.

    c. Complete all assigned schoolwork on time. Communicate if there are any questions or issues.

    d. Be in bed by _____

    e. Other: _____

2. *Behavior*

    a. No name calling.

    b. Pick up after yourself.

    c. Respect others' personal space.

    d. Other: _____

3. *Home*

    a. Complete your chores.

    b. Be respectful.

    c. Listen and follow directions.

    d. Other: _____

4. _____

    a. _____

    b. _____

    c. _____

    d. _____

Rewards and Consequences:

These expectations should be completed at _____% weekly. Try starting small and remember to be realistic. In the following spaces, identify consequences and rewards for each expectation.

1. _____

_____

_____

2. _____

_____

_____

3. _____

_____

_____

4. _____

_____

_____

Family Meeting:

We suggest having a weekly family meeting to discuss progress and make any necessary changes. Here is a structured outline for these meetings:

1. Identify positives for all members of the family. What worked well this week? What improvements did you see? Were there any good surprises?

2. Identify challenges for the week, and choose **one** to focus on during the meeting. Focus on what could be different or how you would like it handled in the future. Validate any small changes you notice in your children's behavior. Create a new weekly goal for each family member.

3. End by restating the positives and acknowledging the hard work that happened during the family meeting. This shows gratitude and appreciation.

Family Meeting Night: _____

Family Meeting Time: _____

Signatures:

Signature: _____

Signature: _____

Signature: _____

Signature: _____

Signature: _____

The Lying Dice

There are many reasons people lie. Sometimes it feels easier to lie in the moment than to tell the truth. Other times, you might think that lying will help you get away with something. However, the reality is that lying can cause a lot of issues. It can make you lose trust with loved ones and even ruin your reputation. Let's talk about times that you have lied, why you lied, and how it has affected you. With a trusted adult, take turns rolling a die and answering the question for the number you roll.

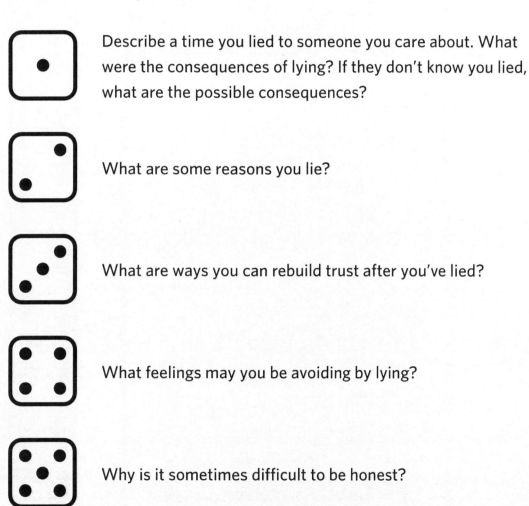

Describe a time you lied to someone you care about. What were the consequences of lying? If they don't know you lied, what are the possible consequences?

What are some reasons you lie?

What are ways you can rebuild trust after you've lied?

What feelings may you be avoiding by lying?

Why is it sometimes difficult to be honest?

Are some people easier to be honest with? Why?

Keep Cool Tools

When you feel overwhelmed, your emotions take over and your brain can't think. During these moments, talking through a problem is *not* going to work! When your emotions become too big, follow the steps here to calm yourself down.

- Name three things you see.
- Do ten jumping jacks.
- Name three things you hear.
- Name your favorite place to visit.
- Run to the end of the hall as fast as you can.
- Take a deep breath in. What do you smell?
- Yell for five seconds.
- Give yourself the biggest hug.
- Other: _____

  _____
- Other: _____

  _____

Creating a Timeline of Events

Big feelings can quickly affect your thoughts, feelings, and behaviors in the moment. Use this worksheet to create a timeline of events that led to your most recent negative or unhelpful behavior. By creating this timeline, you can more easily identify what you could do differently next time so that you can end up with a different outcome. Some examples have been provided for you.

(e.g., being tired or hungry)

1. Vulnerabilities
Things that made you more likely to feel strong emotions

Things I could have done to address some of these vulnerabilities:
(e.g., taken a nap if I was tired, eaten food if I was hungry)

(e.g., I got into a fight with my friend.)

2. Trigger
The thing that set you off or caused the negative behavior

A helpful way that I could have dealt with this trigger:
(e.g., talked to a trusted adult about the fight)

(e.g., I don't need her as a friend anyway.)

3. Thoughts
Things you were thinking at the time

Some helpful ways I could have worked through these thoughts:
(e.g., reminded myself that this relationship is important to me)

4. Emotions
Things you were feeling at the time

(e.g., sad, hurt)

Some ways I could have effectively dealt with these emotions:
(e.g., wrote in my journal, listened to a song that makes me happy)

5. Body Sensations
The physical symptoms you were feeling at the time

(e.g., clenched fists, flushed face)

To help shift these body sensations, I could have:
(e.g., squeezed and released my fists, put some cool water on my face)

6. Negative Behavior
What you did

(e.g., I talked about my friend behind her back.)

More effective things I could have done instead of the negative behavior:
(e.g., talking to my friend directly)

7. Consequences
The outcome of the situation

(e.g., I lost the friendship and feel guilty.)

How things could have been different if I had responded more effectively:
(e.g., I would have felt less guilty and could have possibly repaired my relationship with my friend.)

Relationship Repair

When your emotions take over, you can sometimes hurt the people you care about, including those who are just trying to be helpful. When this happens, it's important that you take the time to repair the relationship. Answer the following questions to reflect on what happened, then write an apology letter to the person you hurt. You can write your own letter or use the outline provided.

Step 1: Reflect on What Happened

- What were the consequences of your actions on the relationship?

- What were you feeling and thinking at the time?

- What can you do to make things between you and the other person better?

- What will you do differently next time to keep this from happening again?

Step 2: Apologize

Dear _____,

I would like to apologize for _____

_____.

I'm sure my behavior may have made you feel _____

_____.

I acted this way because _____

_____.

Next time, I will try _____

_____.

I hope you accept my apology.

Sincerely,

_____

Defining Self-Harm and Self-Injurious Behaviors

> **Note:** Please be aware that the information in this section can be triggering, so if at any point you feel uncomfortable, please make sure to take a break and talk to a trusted adult.

What Is Self-Harm?

Self-harm (or self-injurious behavior) is when someone hurts themselves to deal with painful experiences or memories, overwhelming situations, difficult emotions, or multiple stressors.

Why Do Some People Self-Harm?

Self-harm is frequently used as a temporary solution to deal with problems (e.g., school, work, relationships, emotions). The problem is that self-harming behaviors work in the moment, but they do not solve the actual problem and cause even more issues down the road. People may self-harm to:

- Express something that is difficult to put into words

- Avoid emotional pain by experiencing physical pain

- Feel something different from what they are feeling in the moment

- Escape feelings of numbness or emptiness

- Deal with overwhelming thoughts or feelings

- Escape traumatic memories

- Feel in control of something

- Punish themselves

- Act on suicidal thoughts or urges in a way that will not kill them

What Are Some Types of Self-Harm?

- Cutting

- Burning

- Inserting sharp objects into the body

- Pulling out hair from different areas of the body

- Head banging, punching self or objects, biting, or harming the body

- Getting into situations where one may get hurt

- Hanging, strangulation, or suffocation

- Misusing alcohol, prescriptions, or illegal substances

- Picking or scratching at the skin

- Having unsafe sex

- Binge eating or restrictive eating

Important Things to Consider

Both adolescents and adults can struggle with self-harm and may have difficulty stopping the behavior once they have started. Although it is common for individuals to hide their self-harm, these behaviors can quickly become worse, and no self-harm should be ignored or taken lightly.

If you are struggling with self-harm thoughts or behaviors, please talk to your treatment provider or a trusted adult. You are not alone.

Self-Harm Red Flags

The urge to self-harm can increase quickly. The more aware you become of your warning signs, the quicker you can respond and find other behaviors or solutions that are more helpful. The following list includes possible warning signs, or red flags, for self-harm. Check off the red flags that apply to you or add in your own.

- ☐ Spending more time alone
- ☐ Racing or repeating thoughts
- ☐ Feeling irritable or angry
- ☐ Taking a shower
- ☐ Hiding objects you can use to self-harm
- ☐ Listening to certain types of music
- ☐ Watching certain types of shows or movies
- ☐ Feeling hopeless
- ☐ Feeling numb
- ☐ Wanting to feel something different
- ☐ Having increased urges
- ☐ Feeling "checked out"
- ☐ Feeling excited
- ☐ Using substances

- ☐ Looking for objects you can use to self-harm
- ☐ Feeling strong or overwhelming emotions
- ☐ Changes in eating habits
- ☐ Changes in self-care
- ☐ Wearing long sleeves or pants
- ☐ Feeling down or depressed
- ☐ Withdrawing from family and friends
- ☐ Having issues at school
- ☐ Arguing more with others
- ☐ Feeling like other things are out of control
- ☐ Experiencing significant changes in mood
- ☐ Being reminded of a trauma
- ☐ Other: _____

QUESTIONS

- Which of these red flags happen the most often?
- What makes it difficult to avoid self-harming behaviors?
- What should other people look for as red flags for your self-harm?
- What can others do to support you when you are experiencing multiple red flags?
- What makes it hard for you to talk with others about your red flags?

Before and After

Self-harm can be hard to understand, both for yourself and others. You may struggle to know exactly why you do it, which can cause conflict with the people you care about. However, the reality is that all behaviors (even the unhelpful ones!) meet some need. Use this worksheet to better understand how your self-harm meets your needs.

Step 1: Understanding Your Self-Harm

How do you feel before you self-harm?

_____

_____

_____

How do you feel after? (e.g., relief, shame, guilt)

_____

_____

_____

What triggers lead you to self-harm?

_____

_____

_____

What does self-harm mean to you?

_____

_____

_____

How do you view yourself after you self-harm?

_____

_____

_____

How does your self-harm impact your relationships and the world around you?

_____

_____

_____

Step 2: Drawing Your Self-Harm

Now that you have thought about these different areas, use the following space to draw or creatively write about your self-harm. There is no right or wrong way to do this; the only goal is to gain more understanding. Take your time and ask your treatment provider for assistance if you get stuck. If you notice any big emotions or urges kicking up as you're doing this activity, make sure to take a break and talk with a trusted adult. You can always come back when you're ready.

What Else Can I Do?

Although self-harm is often used as a problem-solving behavior, it usually does not solve the actual problem. The following list can help you work through your urge to self-harm by providing safe alternatives. Check off the solutions you think are most helpful. If you have any questions, be sure to ask your treatment provider for support.

☐ Talk to a supportive person to identify possible solutions.

Name of trusted adult: _____

☐ Try another activity to take your mind off the problem until your strong feelings decrease.

Possible activities: _____

_____

_____

☐ Place a cool rag across your eyes and take some slow, deep breaths to help everything slow down.

☐ When feeling calm, list out the pros and cons of self-harming. Remind yourself of these when you have an urge.

☐ Trying using your five senses to help you relax (e.g., listen to music, watch a show, smell something pleasant, take a shower or bath, exercise).

☐ Walk away from the situation to give yourself a mental and physical break.

☐ Hold ice in your hands and focus your attention on how it feels.

☐ Imagine something peaceful and calming.

Ages 12+

How Do I Stay Safe?

For a safety plan to work, it must be something that you actively take part in creating and are willing to use when needed. The following template can help you create a safety plan for when you're at risk of hurting yourself. Make sure to think of as many different options as possible in case one does not work. Remember, no solution works all the time! If you need help, ask a trusted adult to go through the worksheet with you.

Triggers or warning signs for self-harm

⬇

Ways to distract myself in those moments (e.g., read a book)

⬇

| **Safe people I can call (name and phone number)** | ➡ | **Safe places I can go (name and location)** |

⬇

Things that motivate me to stay safe (e.g., my pet)

⬇

Emergency places to call or go to for additional assistance

Mobile crisis: _____

Suicide prevention hotline: _____

Emergency room: _____

QUESTIONS

- Where can you keep this safety plan to make it easier to use in the moment?
- Who do you want to know about your safety plan?
- What is your motivation to use your safety plan?
- What might make it hard or get in the way of using your safety plan?
- Is there another name you'd like to give your safety plan?

How Can We Keep You Safe?

Safety planning is not just about helping your child identify ways they can keep themselves safe—it's also about providing you and your family with suggestions on how to improve safety and support your child during difficult times. Review the following checklist to identify what could be helpful to keep your child safe and provide support.

☐ Validate whatever your child is struggling with, even if you don't agree or fully understand.

☐ Take all self-harm or reported urges seriously.

☐ Keep open communication between you and your child. Remember, these things may be difficult for both of you to discuss. Take it slow!

☐ Ask questions, but don't bombard them with a lot of questions all at once.

☐ Listen and work to understand the underlying causes of high-risk behaviors. Remember, self-harm is often a solution to a problem!

☐ Keep firm and consistent boundaries and enforce fair consequences. Consistency and structure are key in making children feel secure and emotionally stable.

☐ Don't punish self-harm. Talk to your child's treatment provider about other alternatives.

☐ Normalize struggling with self-harm. Support your child's openness to ask for help.

☐ Get support for yourself and other family members.

☐ Lock up all medications and weapons. Don't assume a "not my child" attitude.

☐ Look for changes in behavior, including changes in interactions, clothing, and personality.

☐ Don't act on emotion! If necessary, give yourself time to breathe and process.

☐ Directly ask your child how you can support them.

☐ Work on learning and understanding your child's warning signs and triggers.

☐ Don't focus solely on the self-harm behavior. Spend time together engaging in positive activities.

Now that you've gone through the checklist, jot down any questions that you may have for your child and your child's treatment provider so you can further discuss them in session.

Questions for my child:

_____

_____

_____

_____

_____

_____

_____

Questions for my child's treatment provider:

_____

_____

_____

_____

_____

_____

_____

_____

_____

Riding the Wave

"Riding the wave" is a skill that can help you ride out negative thoughts, unhelpful urges, and big feelings without acting on them. You ride the wave by using *observe* and *describe* skills.

Observe:

• Observing is about using your five senses (sight, sound, smell, taste, and touch) to notice what is going on both inside and outside of you in this moment.

• You can observe by simply noticing your thoughts, feelings, and urges.

Describe:

• This involves adding words to describe what you observed.

• When describing, you want to make sure to stick to the facts. That means you don't make any judgments or assumptions about what you observed. For example, "I saw a red car" is a description, while "That car is ugly" is a judgment.

• And remember, if you didn't observe it through your five senses, you can't describe it. For example, you can't know what others are thinking or feeling.

Now let's practice! Practice riding the wave by sitting quietly and noticing what you are thinking and feeling in this moment. Notice each feeling and thought rise within you like a wave rises in the ocean. Use words to describe each feeling or thought, making sure to stick to the facts (no judgments!). Then imagine yourself riding on the top of this wave, and continue riding the wave until you get to the shore. As you approach the shore, imagine each emotion and thought getting smaller and smaller, eventually breaking, or flattening out, like a wave. Then get ready as the next wave (i.e., emotion, thought, urge) builds in the ocean.

If the visual of riding a wave doesn't work for you, there are other options! You can visualize your thoughts, feelings, and urges as:

• Train cars coming in and out of view as you sit on a hill and watch them go by

• Items on a conveyor belt, slowly passing by

• Clouds drifting past as you lay on the ground and look up at the sky

Welcome to Self-Sabotage

Most of us have heard the phrase *self-sabotage*, but what does it actually mean? Self-sabotage refers to any self-destructive behavior that creates obstacles for you, causes you to be unhappy, or potentially hurts you. This handout will help you to understand what self-sabotage is and what causes it so you can identify and overcome the behavior.

What Is Self-Sabotage?

- Happens when you get in the way of reaching your goals, whether you know it or not

- Refers to behaviors or thoughts that create problems in your daily life

- Can impact every area of your life

- Lowers your self-confidence

- Leaves you feeling stuck and in a repetitive cycle

Why Do People Self-Sabotage?

- Challenging early life experiences

- Low self-esteem

- Fear of failure

NOTE:

- These behaviors may have helped you survive difficult situations in the past (e.g., unhealthy relationships or a traumatic childhood), but they now cause more problems instead of fixing them.

How Do You Self-Sabotage?

Self-sabotage includes all the actions you take that get in the way of reaching your goals. Take a look at the following list and check off any of the ways you self-sabotage. Then describe why you think you might engage in that behavior, as well as the possible consequences of doing so. An example has been provided for you first.

☐ **Being distant in relationships or "ghosting" other people**

Why: I'm afraid of people leaving and hurting me.

Consequence: I don't have many relationships.

☐ **Giving up or not trying in the first place if something is challenging**

Why: _____

Consequence: _____

☐ **Knowing I'll get in trouble if I do something I'm not supposed to, but choosing to do it anyway**

Why: _____

Consequence: _____

☐ **Procrastinating**

Why: _____

Consequence: _____

☐ **Being on social media too long or too often**

Why: _____

Consequence: _____

☐ **Trying to get into an argument with friends or family on purpose**

Why: _____

Consequence: _____

☐ **Being late or skipping class frequently**

Why: _____

Consequence: _____

☐ **Not taking care of myself (e.g., not eating well, sleeping enough, or keeping up with basic hygiene)**

Why: _____

Consequence: _____

☐ **Refusing to ask for help when I need it**

Why: _____

Consequence: _____

☐ **Blaming others**

Why: _____

Consequence: _____

☐ **Self-harming (e.g., cutting, burning)**

Why: _____

Consequence: _____

Secondary Gain

To get your needs met, you might sometimes engage in behaviors you know are unhelpful, will get you into trouble, or ruin your relationships. Other times, you might show symptoms of depression or anxiety that are difficult to change, even though you want to act otherwise.

    If either of these things happen to you, it may be helpful to explore any secondary gain you are getting from these behaviors or symptoms—in other words, what are these behaviors or symptoms doing that *work for you*? For example, if you get a lot of wanted attention from your parents every time you have a panic attack, you are experiencing "secondary gain" from your anxiety. While secondary gain isn't necessarily bad, it can be helpful to know when it's happening if you are trying to improve your symptoms and behaviors. The following list includes possible ways you can have secondary gain. Circle any that apply to you.

Attention	Popularity	Praise
Time off	Relief	One-on-one time
Avoidance	Money	Good grades
Closer friendships	Physical pleasure	Pity or sorrow
Less responsibilities	Comfort	Medication
Attachment (connection to others)		Labels (e.g., "the depressed kid")

Flags of Safety

To manage and prevent unhelpful behaviors, it's important to know your warning signs and to identify things that can put you in harm's way, as well as what you are already doing to keep yourself safe. In this worksheet, you will work with your treatment provider to identify the red, yellow, and green flags for your problematic behaviors (e.g., self-harm, risky sex, procrastination, skipping school, substance use, restrictive eating). Check the components of each flag that pertain to you, or add in your own in the blank spaces.

My problematic behaviors: _____

RED FLAGS

WARNING! These are signs that there is an immediate problem.

- ☐ Hiding things or lying
- ☐ Not wanting to do things you normally like to do
- ☐ Feeling that nothing matters (good or bad)
- ☐ Isolating yourself from others
- ☐ Other: _____

YELLOW FLAGS

CAUTION! These are signs that there may be a problem.

- ☐ Having overwhelming or racing thoughts
- ☐ Thinking that everything is okay
- ☐ Avoiding helpful people
- ☐ Talking negatively about yourself
- ☐ Noticing consistent changes in your sleep or eating habits
- ☐ Other: _____

GREEN FLAGS | **SAFE!** These are signs that you are doing well.

- ☐ Participating in all appointments
- ☐ Taking all your medications as prescribed
- ☐ Following your schedule
- ☐ Staying in touch with friends and family
- ☐ Having no or low urges to self-harm
- ☐ Being able to observe and work through urges and thoughts in the moment
- ☐ Being able to stay focused on the present
- ☐ Keeping up with your hygiene (e.g., showering, brushing your teeth and hair, changing into clean clothes)
- ☐ Other: _____

QUESTIONS

- What are some things you can do to improve and strengthen your green flags?
- When you notice yellow or red flags, to whom can you turn for support?
- What do you see as your most helpful green flag?
- What do you see as your most dangerous red flag?

Safety Guessing Game

There are lots of different ways to keep yourself safe, both physically and emotionally. In this guessing game, read through each example and circle whether the situation is safe or unsafe!

Buckling your seatbelt as soon as you get in the car

Safe   **Unsafe**

Talking online or texting with strangers

Safe   **Unsafe**

Yelling at your dad while he is driving the car

Safe   **Unsafe**

Asking for alone time

Safe   **Unsafe**

Getting out of the pool when you hear thunder

Safe   **Unsafe**

Letting an adult know when you are approached by a stranger

Safe   **Unsafe**

A friend touching you in your no-touch zone

Safe   **Unsafe**

Hurting your pet

Safe   **Unsafe**

Looking both ways before you cross the street

Safe   **Unsafe**

Saying no to peer pressure

Safe   **Unsafe**

Hurting yourself because you're upset

Safe   **Unsafe**

Listening to your teachers, coaches, and trusted adults

Safe   **Unsafe**

SECTION 5

Worry, Loss, and Trauma

Worry. If you've worked with children or adolescents who struggle with worry, you know how paralyzing the worry can feel. Their thoughts just won't stop and they always seem to zone in on the worst possible outcome. Their whole body feels discomfort and they can't get rid of the pit in their stomach.

Grief. When kids endure a loss, their feelings of grief, confusion, sadness, and anger can get all jumbled into one extremely overwhelming sensation. Kids may experience grief when they lose someone close to them through death, but they can also grieve the loss of an old school, an old friend, or even an old town. Although grief affects everyone differently, children and adolescents can feel like they're on a rollercoaster ride, constantly changing in the ongoing unknown.

Sadness. Kids who feel sad often blame themselves when things don't go quite the way they expected. They may cry, withdraw from loved ones, and stop engaging in activities that used to bring them joy. Some may question why they should continue to live, and others may have thoughts of hurting themselves or others.

Trauma. Most kids have experienced trauma at some point in their life, whether it's getting bullied at school, experiencing their parents divorcing, or being abused by a stranger or loved one. There is not a list that could encompass all the things that can be considered trauma.

Given the prevalence of worry, grief, sadness, and trauma among children and adolescents, this section includes activities and worksheets to help kids identify and work through these emotions. These tools will not only teach them how to cope with difficult feelings and situations, but it will also help them get down to the root of the issue. In addition, we have taken a CBT approach to assist in identifying any faulty thinking.

Ages 7+

Manifest Your Worry

If you could change your worry into something else, what would it be? What would it look like? What would you name it? Use the following space to create your worry with any art materials you'd like. Be creative and detailed, and make sure you don't forget to name it!

My Remote Control

Worry is a natural emotion that we all experience. However, when you worry about things that are out of your control, it can make you feel helpless and angry. Use this worksheet to help you identify what is in your control and what is out of your control. In the controller, write down examples of things that are *in* your control, such as doing your homework. Then, in the circle around the controller, write down examples of things you *don't* have control over, like having homework.

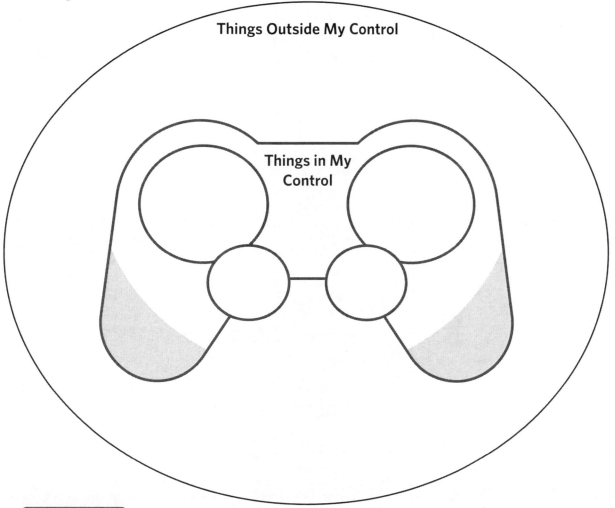

Things Outside My Control

Things in My Control

QUESTIONS

- What is the hardest thing for you to accept that is in your control?
- What is the hardest thing for you to accept that is outside your control?
- What might happen if you only focused on the things you cannot control?
- What are some things you can do to feel more in control?

Worry Toolbox

No one likes to worry! Although you can't make worry go away forever, there are tools you can use to manage your worry. Look at the following list of coping skills and pick the ones you think would be most helpful to you. After choosing your tools, write them in your toolbox. Feel free to add any other tools that aren't listed but are helpful.

Taking deep breaths	Remembering what you have control over
Writing down your worries and coming back to them later	Talking to someone
	Going for a walk
Listening to music	Closing your eyes and imagining your safe place
Watching your favorite movie	
Counting to 10	Other: _____
Taking a break	Other: _____
Coloring	Other: _____

My Worry Dragon

Imagine your worry is like a dragon. The little dragon represents the things that make you worry a little bit, while the big dragon represents the things that make you worry *a lot*. Think about all the things that make you worry and write them on the line beneath the dragons, depending on how big the worry is. Remember, there could be some worries *in between* the two dragons!

_____

_____

_____

_____

_____

_____

_____

Worry Watcher

One way to better understand your worry is to describe, in as much detail as possible, what happens when you feel worried. This way, you can gain more information about what is happening before, during, and after you worry. Use this worksheet to keep track of everything that happens the next time you worry. Then use all your completed trackers to look for patterns and similarities among your different worries!

What was your worry?	**When did your worry occur?** (date and time)

Where were you when you started to worry?	**Who was around?**

How did the worry feel in your body?

- [ ] Really fast thinking
- [ ] Lump in your throat
- [ ] Feeling hot
- [ ] Feeling cold
- [ ] Tight muscles
- [ ] Feeling lightheaded or dizzy
- [ ] Shakiness
- [ ] Butterflies in your stomach
- [ ] Stomachache
- [ ] Difficulty breathing
- [ ] Heart beating fast

Trigger: What happened right before you started to worry?

What did you do after you noticed the worry?

What skills or tools did you use that were helpful?

Path of Grief

Grief is a feeling that happens when you lose something or someone you love. Grief can often feel like a long, winding road with lots of twists and turns. To map out your path of grief, read through the stages of grief and use colored pencils, markers, or crayons to color in whatever color fits each stage. Then cut the stages out and place them along your path of grief on the next page.

DENIAL
It's hard for you to believe this situation has happened. You cannot imagine being okay with the change.

ANGER
You feel angry because of the situation. You may isolate, push others away, or lash out.

BARGAINING
You begin to wonder if there is anything you can do to get the situation back to how it used to be.

DEPRESSION
You feel really sad because you realize you can't change the situation. You find it difficult to feel anything other than sad and stuck.

ACCEPTANCE
You begin to understand and accept the situation. You try to move forward.

QUESTIONS

- Which stage of grief do you feel like you are in right now?
- Which stage do you think is the hardest for you?
- What kinds of support do you need to help you on your path of grief?

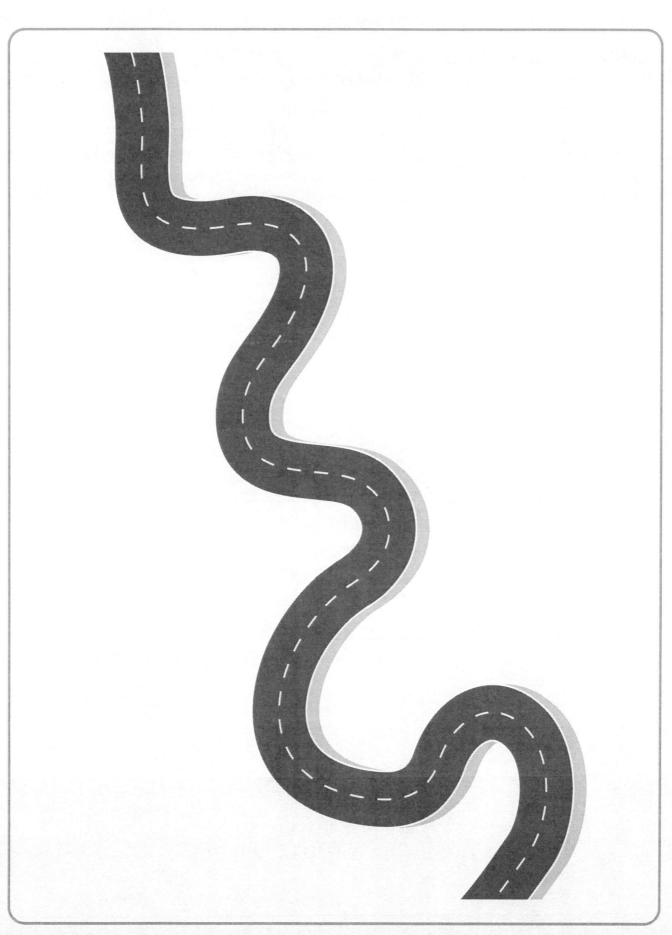

Memory Soup

When you lose someone you love, it is important to remember the positive memories from your time together. Just like soup is made up of many different ingredients, your love for someone is made up of many different memories. Consider some of the positive memories that make up your love for your lost loved one, and write the most special ones in the soup bowl below.

Remember, your memories are the one thing that can't be taken away from you.

Hold on tight!

New World

When you lose someone (or something) you care about, it may feel like your world has ended. Part of moving forward is figuring out which parts of your "old world" you can take with you as you create a "new world" without the person or thing that you lost. In the pieces that make up the following "world," write down all the things you can take with you from your old world (e.g., adventures, traditions, habits, jokes, sayings) into your new world. Thinking of moving forward can be hard, so make sure you take your time completing this worksheet.

QUESTIONS

- Is there anything that is getting in the way of creating a new world for yourself?
- Is there anything you need from others to help you create this new world?
- What do you think the loved one you lost would want to see as a part of your new world?

Drops of Grief

After experiencing grief and loss, it is normal to have big feelings, and many of them can come up unexpectedly. Just like an umbrella protects you from the rain, you have skills that can protect you from the pain of grief and loss. In the cloud, write down the person or part of your life that you have lost. In the raindrops, write down the difficult emotions you are experiencing (or unexpected situations that are triggering you) because of the loss. Finally, on the umbrella, write down the skills you can use, people you can go to, or things you can do to cope with grief.

Ages 8+

Walk Down Memory Lane

One of the biggest worries people have when they lose someone they love is that they will forget all the amazing things they love about that person. This worksheet can help you remember and hold tightly onto those things. Feel free to share your answers or work together with a trusted adult to complete the prompts.

When I think of _____, **I think about:**

My favorite memory of all time: _____

The first thing that comes to mind: _____

What I am going to miss most: _____

A smell that reminds me of them: _____

Their favorite food: _____

Their favorite drink: _____

My favorite physical feature of theirs: _____

My favorite characteristic of theirs: _____

Their personality: _____

Their nickname for me: _____

Their favorite hobby: _____

What they believed in: _____

My favorite saying of theirs: _____

How I picture them: _____

How they made me feel: _____

Quilt of Sadness

Sometimes when you've felt sad, or even depressed, for a long time, you get used to feeling that way. Being sad can become your "normal." Overcoming these feelings and moving forward can be hard. On each piece of the following quilt, write down an example of something that makes you sad *or* something that brings you joy and happiness. Once you have filled in the entire quilt, pick one color for all the "sad" pieces and another color for all the "happy" pieces. Then take a look at how much of your quilt represents your sad feelings versus how much of your quilt makes you happy. What are some things you can do to fill your quilt with more happy pieces?

Ages 8+

The Many Faces of Sadness

Sadness can sometimes be a difficult emotion to feel and to express. While people often associate sadness with someone who is crying, frowning, or acting withdrawn, it can look many other ways! Sometimes, you can look angry or frustrated, even though deep down you are actually sad. The following faces show the many different ways that sadness can look. Circle the faces that show how you express your sadness.

QUESTIONS

- What can make it hard to show your sadness?
- With whom can you share your sadness?
- What are some reasons your face (on the outside) may look different from how you feel (on the inside)?

Turn Your Frown Upside Down

Although it is okay to feel sad, there are also things you can do to cheer yourself up. Below is a wheel of activities that can help you turn your frown upside down! Come up with some of your own ideas for activities and add them in the blank spaces. Then attach the arrow using a thumbtack or pin and give it a spin to help you pick an activity when you're feeling sad!

LET'S TRY . . .

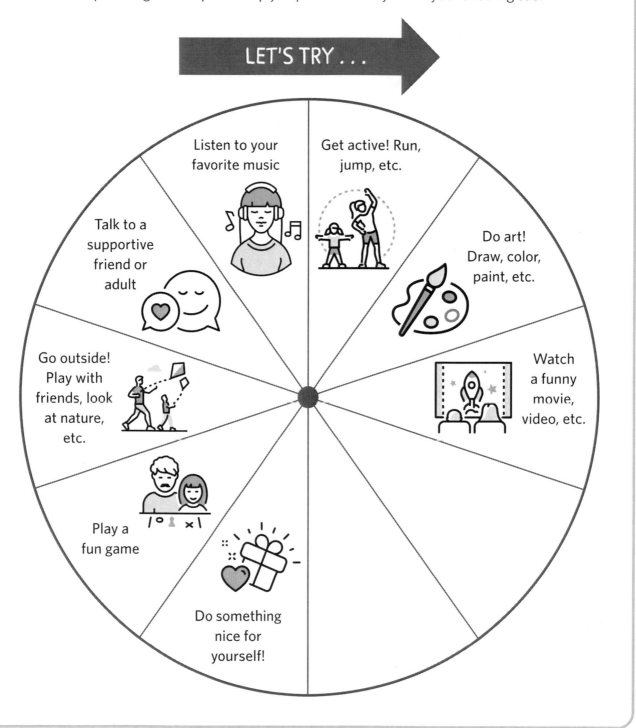

Ages 5+

My Sadness Monster

Do you ever wonder what happens to your body when you feel sad? Sometimes, it can feel like a monster has taken over. Inside the following outline, create your own sadness monster. Color it in, give it a face, and name it!

QUESTIONS

- What makes your sadness monster feel sad?
- How does your sadness monster make your body feel on the inside (e.g., stomachache, feeling tired, tears in your eyes, sad thoughts)?
- How does your sadness monster make you behave on the outside?
- What makes your sadness monster feel better?
- Is there anything others can do to help your sadness monster feel better?

What Does Trauma Mean to You?

Trauma can be difficult to understand and even harder to define. First, let's define what trauma means to *you*. Write or draw your answer in the space provided here.

> Trauma is . . .

Now, let's look at some myths and facts about trauma. Next to each statement, indicate whether you believe it is true or false. On the next page, we will review your answers.

_____ 1. Trauma is how you interpret an event.

_____ 2. Trauma is your fault.

_____ 3. No one will ever love you if you've experienced trauma.

_____ 4. Trauma should be kept a secret.

_____ 5. You can heal from trauma.

_____ 6. You will get over trauma if you stop thinking about it.

_____ 7. The world is a dark and scary place.

_____ 8. Trauma only happens in childhood.

_____ 9. If you've gone through trauma, you are weak, helpless, or scared.

_____ 10. Your trauma defines who you are.

Answer Key:

1. **True:** Trauma is how you interpret an event. At times, this is what makes it hard to define trauma because there is no list of *all* the "bad" things that can happen to you. In a way, this is a good thing because no one can tell you what is or isn't traumatic to you, and no one can tell you how you should feel or think about a particular event.

2. **False:** Trauma is *never* your fault! People don't ask for bad things to happen to them, so how can something that you have no control over be your fault?

3. **False:** If someone can't love *all* of you, then they don't deserve you! Don't let anyone make you feel less than because you have been through something hard.

4. **False:** People are made to feel like their trauma should be kept a secret, which is totally inaccurate. Although trauma isn't something you post on a billboard, it is definitely yours to share with safe and supportive loved ones in a safe and supportive environment.

5. **True:** Although there is no easy way to heal from trauma, it is definitely possible, and you totally deserve to heal! Don't let others or your own negative thinking stand in the way of your healing process.

6. **False:** If healing was that easy, many therapists would be out of a job. (And if it wasn't that big of a deal, then it wouldn't be called trauma!) This statement is simply not true.

7. **False:** Trauma can make it feel like everything in the world is scary and dangerous, but just because it feels that way doesn't always make it true. Trauma changes your brain and can make you think that everything in the world is bad.

8. **False:** Trauma can unfortunately happen at any point, to anyone, regardless of race, gender, culture, income level, religious beliefs, and more.

9. **False:** Going through a traumatic event certainly does not make you weak, helpless, or scared! It means you're resilient, strong, and courageous for surviving the trauma.

10. **False:** Although trauma does not define you, it is still a part of you and your story. It is something that has happened to you, just like the more positive memories and experiences in your life. All your experiences make you who you are!

After learning a little bit more about the myths and facts about trauma, use the space provided here to write or draw what trauma means to you now:

Trauma is . . .

Trauma Triangle

Trauma is hard to deal with! Use the following diagram to describe how trauma affects your thoughts (what you think in your head), feelings (how you feel on the inside), and behaviors (how you act on the outside). Write down a specific trauma memory you want to work on in the space marked "My trauma." Then write down any thoughts, feelings, and behaviors you struggle with because of your trauma in each area of the triangle.

QUESTIONS

- Are there any thoughts, feelings, or behaviors getting in the way of working through your trauma? Which ones?
- Are your thoughts based on facts? If not, how could you change them to make them more factual?
- Are your feelings easy to handle, or do they sometimes feel too big? Is there anything that helps when your feelings take over?
- Are your behaviors helpful or unhelpful? If they're not helpful, what are some other behaviors you could try?
- How do you think the triangle will change after you have worked on your trauma?

Ages 10+

Timeline Highway

Trauma can make you feel stuck in your thoughts and feelings. On the highway below, create a timeline of the most important things (good *and* not-so-good) that have happened in your life. You can start the timeline at any point in your life that you'd like, but make sure to end the timeline with something you want to accomplish in the future. Whenever you write down any not-so-good things that have happened, think about these questions: Who was there for you? How did you get through it? What kept you going? What you were feeling and thinking? What did you want or need at the time?

EXPERIENTIAL USE

Write down each life event on an index card and lay the cards out on the floor to make a timeline. Move from card to card as if you are moving through your life. As you reach each card, ask yourself the same series of questions above.

Ages 12+

Lenses

Trauma can change you and how you see the world. Use the following glasses to create your own pair of "trauma sunglasses." Think about how your beliefs, worries, fears, and ability to trust others has changed from before the trauma up until this current moment. Inside the lenses, write or draw how your trauma has affected you and how it has changed your view on the world.

- Can you identify any unhelpful thoughts in your sunglasses? Is it possible that any of your thoughts are not based on fact?
- What do you think would happen if you took off your trauma sunglasses?
- Is there anything getting in the way of taking off your trauma sunglasses?

Pizza Me

When you experience trauma, it can seem like the trauma is the only thing that makes you who you are. However, you are actually made up of a bunch of different parts. For example, you may have a part of you who doesn't feel good enough and another part who loves music. You can think of your parts like pieces of a pizza, where each separate piece is also a part of the whole. Use the following pizza dough to create and label the pieces that make up your inner parts. A word bank is provided to help you get started, but feel free to write in your own words! Remember, no parts of you are bad, and all parts were created to keep you safe.

Sad	Lonely	Multitasker	Bossy	Spiritual	Happy
Anxious	Caring	Artistic	Assertive	Judging	Bully
Questioning	Scared	Criticized	Lazy	Healthy	Rule-follower
Angry	Funny	Adventurous	Rebellious	Carefree	Smart

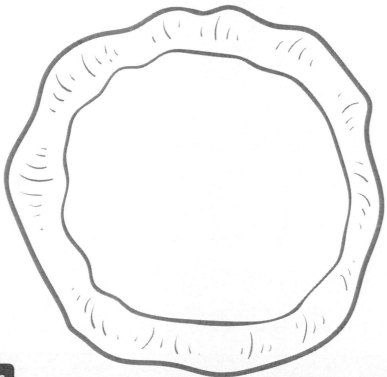

QUESTIONS

- Which part of you feels the most comfortable? The most uncomfortable?
- Which part of you feels like the biggest piece of you?
- Which part of you isn't seen as much as the others?

Life Transitions, Family Dynamics, and Divorce

Kids can go through several adjustments as they grow up, whether it's changing schools, moving to a different town, adjusting to their parents getting divorced, or having a new sibling added to the family. While some kids may adjust well to these transitions, others may struggle. This is especially the case when life transitions involve an unexpected change in family dynamics, such as a divorce or separation. Divorce can be challenging, not only for the children involved, but also for the parents. No matter the situation, it is important to *keep the child first*. Therefore, this section includes several tools to help children navigate significant life changes, including separation and divorce, as well as tools to help adults support a healthy co-parenting relationship and stay focused on the children's best interests.

As family structures change, it is also important to emphasize to children that it is okay for families to look different. Sometimes kids grow up with both of their biological parents. Other times, they grow up with stepparents or even grandparents as their primary caregivers. Family dynamics may also shift during the course of a child's development, which brings its own set of challenges. Therefore, we have also included tools to help children process through their own feelings and thoughts related to any changing family dynamics.

Ages
7+

Comic Strip Stories

Sometimes it can be tough to talk about big life changes that have happened to you. To help you share your point of view, create a comic about a difficult change that you've gone through. You can use the following comic strips or create your own. Choose characters to play the people in your story and draw them out! You can even rewrite the ending if you'd like. Once you're done, share your comic strip story with a trusted adult.

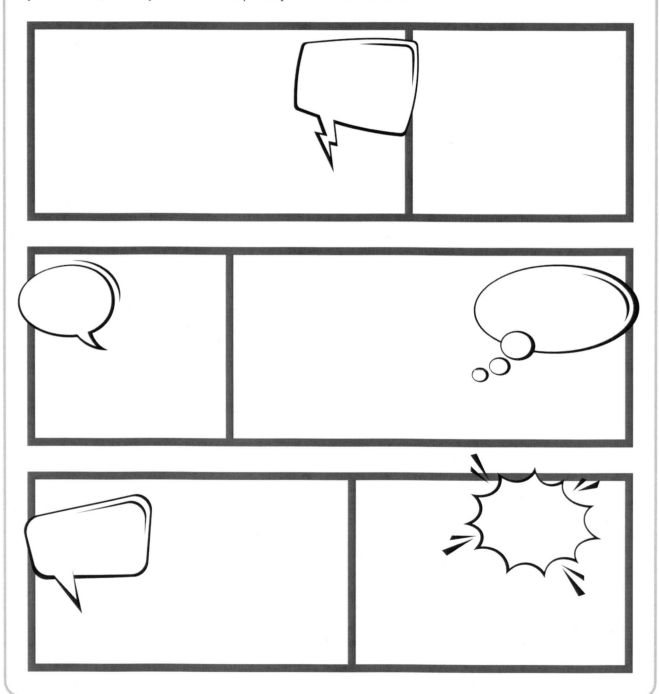

Before, Now, and After

Change is tough! One thing that can help you work through a change you are going through is to talk about how things were before, how they are now, and how you hope they will be after. In the first train car, describe a change that's happening in your life. In the second car, write down how things were *before* the change. In the third car, write down the thoughts and feelings you are having about the change right *now*. Finally, in the last car, write down how you wish things will look *after* the change. An example train has been provided for you first, followed by a blank train for you to fill out!

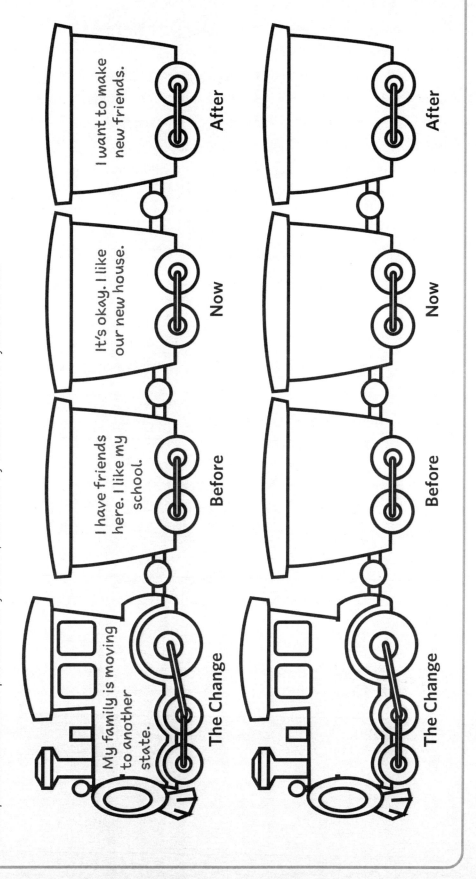

The Change — My family is moving to another state.

Before — I have friends here. I like my school.

Now — It's okay. I like our new house.

After — I want to make new friends.

The Change

Before

Now

After

Safety Bag

Although change can be scary, it's also a normal part of life. To help you feel safer with the change you're going through, create a safety bag so that no matter where you go, you have what you need to feel safe, confident, and comfortable. Get creative with your bag by drawing or writing all the things you need to feel safe, like a favorite blanket or toy, music, photos, lotion, certain people, and so much more. Although you might not have control over the change, you *are* in control of what makes you feel safe.

Dear Me

No matter what changes happen in life, it is important to remember who you are and who you want to be. If you are struggling with a change right now, use the following space to write a letter to your future self—the version of you who has already overcome this struggle. In the letter, be sure to mention the things you love about yourself right now, the skills you've used to get you through hard times, and the things in life that are important to you. You can also share anything else you'd like with your future self!

Dear me:

Looking Back

As adults, we often try to fix our own parents' mistakes, but in doing so, we can get caught up in our past experiences and lose sight of what is important as we parent our own children. This worksheet will help you look at your own childhood to better understand how you parent now.

How do you remember feeling about your parents when you were younger?

_____

_____

_____

_____

_____

What are things you have tried to do differently with your own child?

_____

_____

_____

_____

_____

When you became a parent, what is one thing you said you would never do? Where do you stand on that point now?

_____

_____

_____

_____

_____

Is there anything your parents did in your childhood that you would like to continue to do as a parent?

_____

_____

_____

_____

Are there any changes you feel you need to make as a parent? Why or why not?

_____

_____

_____

_____

Perspectives and Compromises

When there is conflict in the family system, it can be difficult for each side to see other peoples' perspectives. To help you gain perspective regarding the needs of your family, have each member of the family fill in this worksheet, and then use the discussion points at the end to find a compromise that both sides can agree upon.

PARENT'S PERSPECTIVE:

- What are important characteristics for you to have in your family system?
- What do you think you are currently missing from your family system?
- What is your role within the family system? Do any changes need to be made to your role? If so, why?
- List the attributes about each family member that you like.
- List one thing you would change about each family member.
- What are the current consequences in the household? Are the consequences effective?
- What is the biggest change you wish you could see in your family?
- What is something that you can let go of?

CHILD'S PERSPECTIVE:

- What are important things for you to have in your family?
- What do you think you are currently missing from your family?
- What part do you play in your family? Do any changes need to be made to your part? If so, why?
- List the things you like about each family member.
- List one thing you would change about each family member.
- What are "fair" consequences or consequences you'd like to see used in your family?
- If you could make three rules, what would they be?
- What is one thing you wish everyone understood about you?

FIND COMPROMISE:

- How were your answers similar?
- How were your answers different?
- What are some areas you can find room to compromise?
- What is one thing everyone can do that can contribute to the family's healing process?

Parenting Fears

Parenting can be scary enough in its own right—even more so when you are navigating a big life transition. Even though you might try to set boundaries and expectations, there are many things outside of your control, such as whether your child will always make good decisions or stumble with the occasional misstep. Use the following space to identify the fears you have for your child, especially those that are getting in the way of your ability to parent effectively. Then use the reflection questions to explore how to manage these fears. Be specific and dig deep.

_____

_____

_____

_____

_____

_____

_____

_____

_____

_____

EXPERIENTIAL USE

Write down your child's fears on various index cards, or use various objects around the home or therapy office to represent these fears. Then, have the child place these fears into a basket and process how to best overcome them.

QUESTIONS

- How have you allowed these fears to stand in the way of your parenting so far?
- What kind of parent would you be without any fear?
- What needs to change so that you can release your fear?

Parenting Control Circles

When you're going through a big life change, it can be tempting to try to control your child in situations where both of you have no control. Think about the last argument or conflict you had with your child in relation to a big change, such as a recent move, the birth of a sibling, or a new visitation schedule. Then use the circles to identify what you have control over in this situation and what is not possible to control and record them in the corresponding areas.

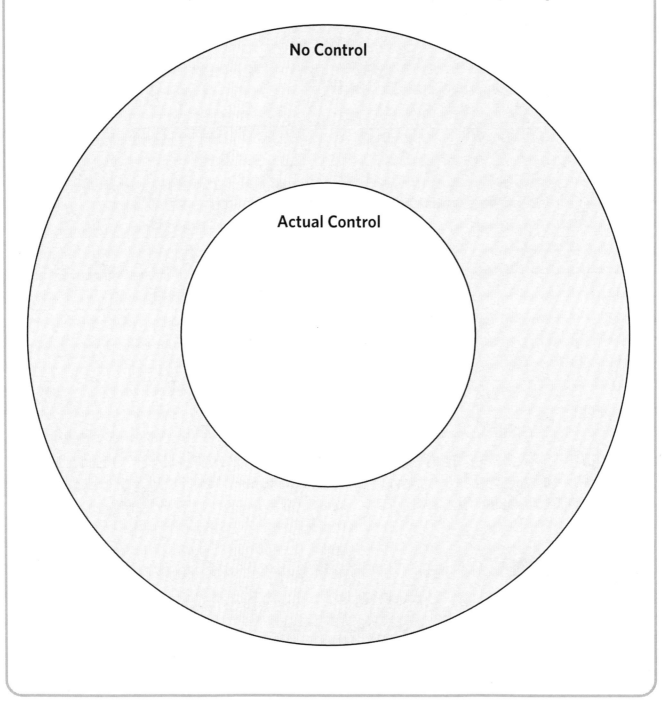

No Control

Actual Control

Shared Space

You cannot control everything your child does, nor should you. You also can't control how they respond to major life changes. To help you learn how to share space, think of a recent family transition that is currently causing conflict within your family. For example, perhaps your child is acting out after a recent move, birth, death, or loss in the family. To help you better navigate this situation, follow the prompts in the following diagram to identify and write down specific areas that you need to maintain control, share control, and give up control when it comes to parenting. The area in the middle will be the new "shared space" you can use to parent more effectively. Remember that transitions can be challenging for kids, and by finding areas you can lighten up control and compromise, you can help your child adjust to the situation more easily.

Areas where you need to maintain control (e.g., curfew or grades)

Areas where you are willing to share control and compromise

Areas where you can give your child more independence to make their own choices (e.g., clothes or hair color)

Ages 10+

Two Houses, Two Perspectives

Divorce and separation are hard, but what makes it even harder is when your parents argue or put you in the middle of their conflict. Even though your parents are going to disagree, it doesn't mean they don't love you. Use this worksheet to talk about what life looks like at each of your parent's homes. Write down the different rules and expectations they each have for you in each of the following areas. Then, in the middle column, write down what you would like each of these areas to look like.

_____'s House	My Voice	_____'s House
School:		School:
Friendships:		Friendships:
Dating:		Dating:
Extracurriculars:		Extracurriculars:
Technology:		Technology:
Chores/Responsibilities:		Chores/Responsibilities:
Medical care:		Medical care:
Self-expression:		Self-expression:
Punishment:		Punishment:

Ages 7+

What Feels Equal?

When your parents no longer live together in the same house, you might have to travel back and forth, and spending time between two homes doesn't always feel fair or equal. Use the following monthly calendar to write down what you wish your schedule would look like each week, making sure to use a specific colored marker, pen, or pencil to represent each of your two homes. For example, do you wish that you could alternate full weeks at each house? Or do you prefer to rotate between houses every three or four days? Or would you hope for a different type of setup? What feels fair and equal to you?

Sunday	Monday	Tuesday	Wednesday	Thursday	Friday	Saturday

QUESTIONS

- When it comes to holidays, what does fair and equal look like to you?
- What about your birthday? Your other family members' birthdays?
- What about extracurricular activities?
- What do you think each parent wants your schedule to look like?

Listen

When there is conflict within your family, kids sometimes don't get a chance to express how they are feeling, which can leave them feeling unheard and misunderstood. This activity will give you the space to freely write about everything that is going on with your family—the things you dislike, disagree with, or feel misunderstood about. Use this as an opportunity to express your wants, needs, and opinions about the situation. Feel free to write whatever comes to your mind. If you'd like, you can express your ideas creatively through a song, poem, or other art form.

Lead the Way

Sometimes, the most effective way to resolve family conflict is to overcome *other* challenges together. In this activity, you'll work together in pairs to help your partner navigate their way through an obstacle course while wearing a blindfold. The goal of the game is to make sure your partner makes it through the course in the least time possible without touching any of the obstacles. If they touch any obstacles, the course must be started over. Here are the steps to play:

1. Gather whatever objects you'd like to make your own obstacle course—such as yarn, rope, chairs, books, magazines, stuffed animals, cones, or tape—and lay it out on the ground in a random pattern. Get creative! Just keep in mind to not make it too dangerous or difficult.

2. After you have created the course, family members will be broken into pairs. This can be done by drawing names, picking numbers, or choosing partners—whatever works.

3. Once partners have been identified, you may start the race! One partner should be blindfolded, while their partner is responsible for verbally guiding them through the course.

4. Feel free to take turns guiding and navigating, switch up partners, change the rules, and even identify rewards for winners.

After completing the obstacle course, gather as a family to discuss the following questions. Make sure to allow everyone to answer each question and share their opinions.

QUESTIONS

- What was difficult about this activity?
- What do you feel you did well?
- How do you think this activity can help with communication among family members?
- Are there any ways where you feel like you made progress with your partner?

My Side of the Story

When working through your parents' divorce or separation, your voice is important. Fill in the following blanks to tell *your* side of the story. If there is something you want to say that is not included here, be sure to add it so you can tell your full story.

My name is _____. I am _____ years old.

My mom and dad are _____

_____.

They divorced when I was _____ years old.

When they were together, they would _____

_____.

We did these fun things together: _____

_____.

Since the divorce, I spend _____ with Mom.

Mom lives _____.

I like it when Mom _____

_____.

I don't like it when Mom _____

_____.

I talk to Mom about _____

_____.

I worry about _____

_____ .

Mom makes me feel _____

_____ .

Since the divorce, I spend _____ with Dad.

Dad lives _____

_____ .

I like it when Dad _____

_____ .

I don't like it when Dad _____

_____ .

I talk to Dad about _____

_____ .

I worry about _____

_____ .

Dad makes me feel _____

_____ .

When I think of my parents' divorce, I often feel _____ .

and I wish _____

_____

because _____

_____ .

I feel like _____ listens to me and understands me.

One thing I wish that everyone would understand is _____

_____.

I want to tell my parents _____

_____.

I feel angry when _____

_____.

When I am angry, I _____

_____.

I feel loved when _____

_____.

_____ makes me feel loved.

As I move forward in life, I want to _____,

and _____ is what I can do about it.

I want both of my parents to _____

_____.

It is important that both of my parents know _____

_____.

What Is My Role?

Sometimes it can be confusing to know what your role is in a divorce or separation. You might think you're supposed to act one way, but this may conflict with what other people tell you or with your idea of how you think it "should" be. This can make you feel like you're stuck in the middle. Use this worksheet to explore what you have been told about your role—from your parents, your relatives, social media, TV shows, and even from yourself—and then compare those lists to the *actual* role you have as a kid going through this change.

What Have Others Told You Your Role Is?	What Do You Think Your Role Is?	Your Actual Role
		• Not taking sides or having to pick sides • Staying out of the drama • Being honest • Openly talking about your feelings, worries, and questions • Understanding that expectations are different at your two homes • Taking care of yourself • Remembering you should always feel like you, just with two homes, with two families that love you no matter what

Roles We Play

What role do you play in your family? Are you the "protector" or the "funny one"? Are you the scapegoat (the person everyone blames) or the parent figure (even though you're a kid)? Complete one or both of the following activities to define the role or roles you have in your family, as well as the roles everyone else in your family has.

ACTIVITY #1:

Use sand tray figurines, puppets, dolls, or other toys to represent each member of your family, including yourself. Think figuratively—not literally! Talk about why you selected the specific toy you chose for each person.

- What made you pick each toy for your family members? What qualities are similar between the toys you picked and each family member?

- Are there any toys you wish you'd found that would better represent each family member? If so, what would they be and why would you pick them?

- How would all the toys you picked get along with each other?

- If you could trade places with anyone in your family, who would it be and why?

ACTIVITY #2:

Draw, paint, or use sculpting dough to create each member of your family, including yourself. Get creative and think about what roles they play! For example, if the mom in a family made all the decisions, you could draw her as a judge!

- Describe your art. How did you choose to represent each family member in this way?

- How did it feel to create art about your family?

- If your family had to represent you with art, what do you think it would look like?

Ages 5+

My Family Portrait

When parents get divorced, they don't typically ask you what you want your family picture to look like. You may imagine that it will be one way, but then it ends up looking another way. No matter where you are in the process of understanding your parents' divorce, your opinion matters. Use this picture frame to draw what you want your family portrait to look like. You can complete this worksheet multiple times to see if your family picture changes over time or how you might want it to change over time.

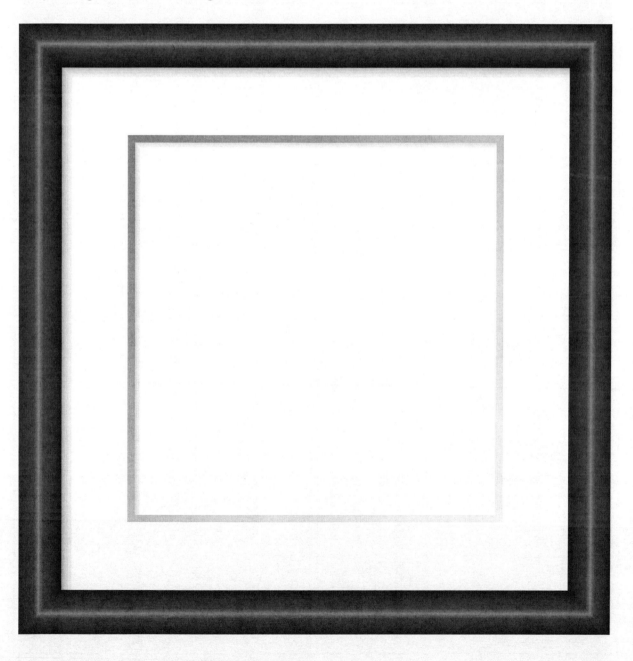

Pros and Cons

It isn't easy going through a big family change like a parental divorce or separation. To help you process your feelings about this change, it can be helpful to talk about the tough parts (the "cons"), as well as the good parts (the "pros"). Take some time to think of some pros and cons about your parents' divorce or separation and write them in each column. Some examples have been provided for you.

👍 Pros	👎 Cons
No yelling and fighting in the house every day	I don't get to see mom and dad every day

Conversation Starters

Having a blended family can feel weird and awkward, especially at the beginning when you're still getting to know each other. This activity can provide you with ideas to start conversations with your new family members, which is often the hardest part. Take turns with your family members answering the following questions. Use the blank boxes to come up with ideas for your own conversation starters.

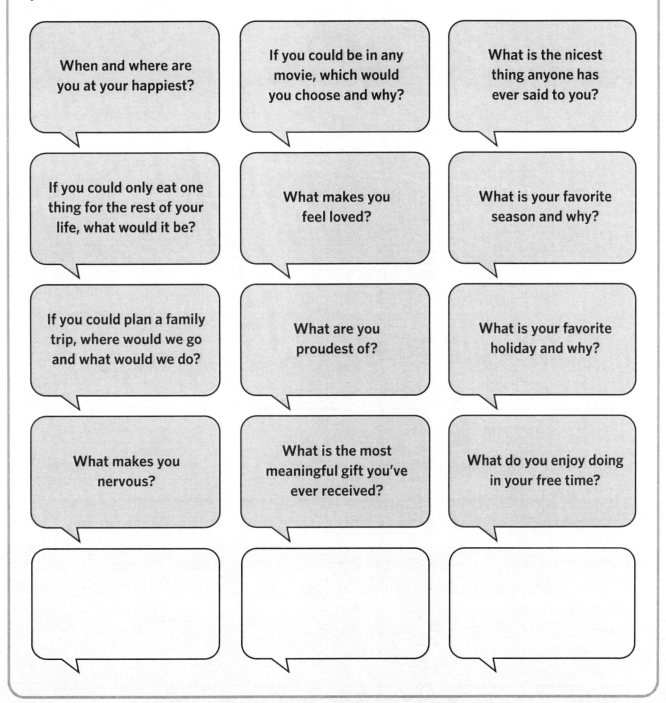

When and where are you at your happiest?

If you could be in any movie, which would you choose and why?

What is the nicest thing anyone has ever said to you?

If you could only eat one thing for the rest of your life, what would it be?

What makes you feel loved?

What is your favorite season and why?

If you could plan a family trip, where would we go and what would we do?

What are you proudest of?

What is your favorite holiday and why?

What makes you nervous?

What is the most meaningful gift you've ever received?

What do you enjoy doing in your free time?

The "Blended" Family

While blending families can be challenging, it is also an opportunity to bring together all the things you love about *both* families. To help you create your blended family, identify all the things that you would like to "blend" together from each side of the family. For example, there might be family vacations, special occasions, rules, or certain celebrations that you want to bring together.

Summer trip to the beach

QUESTIONS

- Was there anything challenging about this activity? Why or why not?
- What is one thing from each family that you are excited to "blend" with your current family?
- What makes blending difficult? What seems to not work?
- How will you know when your blended family is working well together?

SECTION 7

Setting Boundaries and Building Healthy Relationships

A boundary is a defining line that marks the limits of an area. It often represents where one thing ends and another begins. When kids have boundaries that are too loose, people can take advantage of them, and when they have boundaries that are too rigid, it makes it hard to establish healthy relationships. Given that learning how to set and enforce healthy boundaries is an important step in developing healthy relationships, this section includes a variety of activities that help children explore boundaries, including how to create them, what they look like in different settings, and how to put them into practice.

These tools will help kids develop relationships that are reciprocal in nature and grounded in reassurance, acceptance, and encouragement. When relationships are one-sided, things can feel off balance, so it is important that kids learn how to communicate their needs when they are stressed, overwhelmed, or hurt. Doing so creates a space where they can feel supported and also have the ability to support others.

Finally, given that trust is a foundational component of healthy relationships, we have included several tools to facilitate rupture and repair when trust has been broken in a relationship. Building trust takes time, especially once it is lost. We tell families that it takes about six months to earn an inch of trust. That's a long time! But trust is crucial in the context of healthy relationships.

Ages 13+

My Boundaries

A boundary is a limit that you set on what you're okay with versus what you're not okay with. Although boundaries can look different for everyone, it is important to set boundaries that keep your needs and wants balanced. This worksheet will help you think about the boundaries that are important to you in different life areas so you can stay on track. In each circle, write down what boundaries you'd like to set in that area of your life. Some examples have been provided for you.

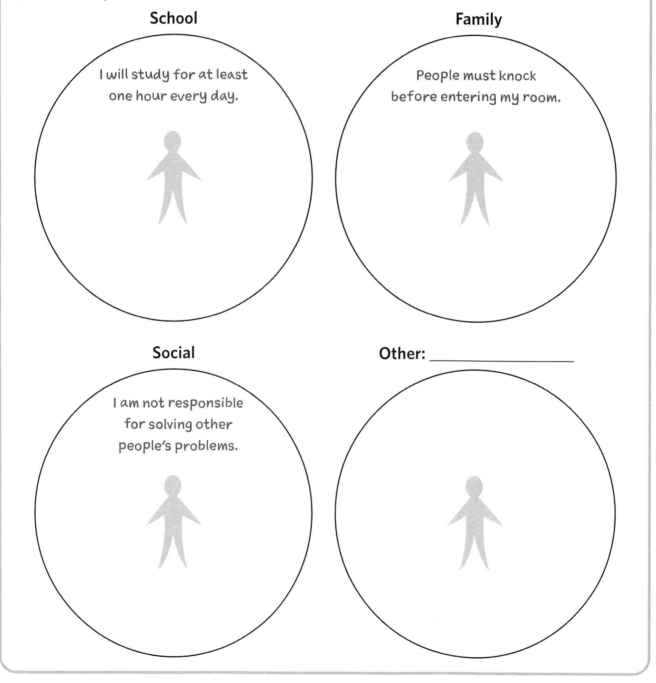

School

I will study for at least one hour every day.

Family

People must knock before entering my room.

Social

I am not responsible for solving other people's problems.

Other: _____

Value and Boundary Sort

Your values are the things that are important to you in life. Below you will find a list of common values. Describe how important each value is to you, then identify one boundary you have (or one that you can set) to protect this value and remain true to who you are. An example has been provided for you first.

Core Values	Level of Importance (Very Important, Important, Not Important)	Boundary
Academics	Important	I do all my homework before playing with friends
Adventure		
Balance		
Beauty		
Compassion		
Creativity		

Core Values	Level of Importance (Very Important, Important, Not Important)	Boundary
Determination		
Fairness		
Faith		
Family		
Friendship		
Fun		
Growth		
Happiness		

Core Values	Level of Importance (Very Important, Important, Not Important)	Boundary
Honesty		
Independence		
Knowledge		
Leadership		
Love		
Loyalty		
Popularity		
Respect		

Healthy Boundaries

Knowing how to set healthy boundaries is a tough skill to learn. Even adults can struggle with this sometimes! To help you understand the difference between healthy and unhealthy boundaries, complete the chart below by describing whether each scenario is an example of a healthy or unhealthy boundary and explaining the reasoning behind your answer.

Boundary	Healthy/Unhealthy	Why
I have to answer the phone every time someone calls.		
I can't say no to anyone.		
It's okay to put myself and my needs first.		
My mom is my best friend.		
I can be honest with my job when I am overwhelmed with school.		

Boundary	Healthy/Unhealthy	Why
I have to share everything with everyone.		
It is important to have balance between school, home, and social activities.		
It is important to try my best in school—I don't have to be perfect.		
I have to accept all friend requests and followers on all social media outlets.		

QUESTIONS

- Do you feel like you have more healthy or unhealthy boundaries?
- Which unhealthy boundary impacts you the most and why?
- Why it is harder to set healthy boundaries?
- What do you do if your boundaries are different from the people who matter to you?

Stop Sign

Boundaries are flexible and can change depending on the situation or people involved. In order for people to respect your boundaries, it is important to brainstorm how to communicate these boundaries in a variety of settings and with different people. The following stop signs represent different ways you can set boundaries. Finish each sentence with an example of a boundary you would like to be able to talk about. There is also a blank stop sign for you to add your own unique boundaries. An example has been provided for you first.

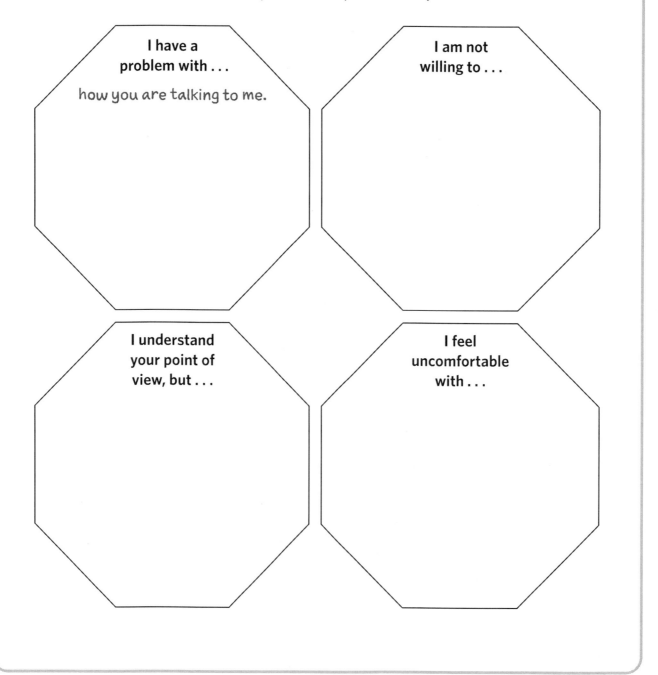

I have a
problem with . . .

how you are talking to me.

I am not
willing to . . .

I understand
your point of
view, but . . .

I feel
uncomfortable
with . . .

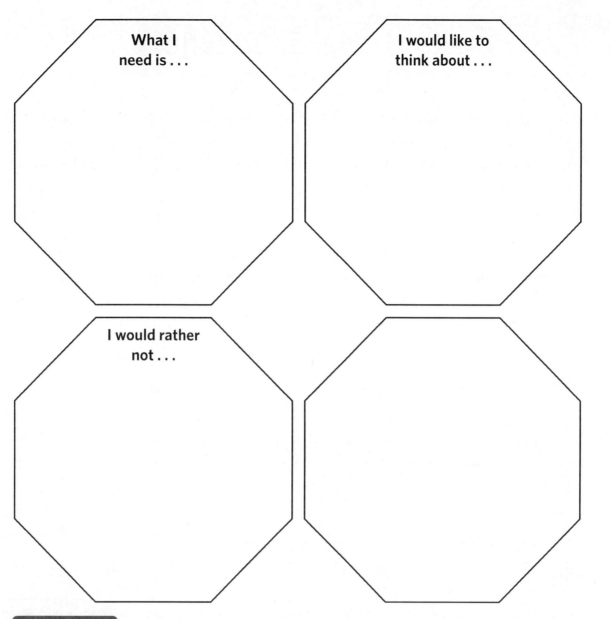

**What I
need is . . .**

**I would like to
think about . . .**

**I would rather
not . . .**

QUESTIONS

- In what situations, or with what people, would setting these boundaries be most difficult? Practice what it would be like to use these boundaries.
- Pretend that a friend asks you to do something you do not agree with. How could you use one of the previous boundaries to communicate how you feel?
- What was a situation where the boundary you set needed to be changed because of the circumstances?
- When was a time you tried to set a boundary unsuccessfully? Who was involved, what boundary did you try to set, and what did you say? Try rephrasing the boundary now that you have learned these new skills.

Relational Boundaries

A boundary is a dividing line that separates two things. Relational boundaries are key to having healthy relationships because they keep your needs and wants balanced. There are many different types of boundaries you can set in relationships, including emotional, physical, mental, sexual, and financial. Read through the different types of boundaries and rate how you think you're doing with regard to each boundary on a scale of 1–5 (with 1 being "not so great" and 5 being "really well"). Remember that you can always revisit and modify the boundaries in any relationship, for whatever reason you feel necessary.

1. **Emotional boundaries** involve separating your feelings from other's feelings. You may have weak emotional boundaries if you take responsibility for another person's feelings, blame others for how you feel, deny your own feelings, or put others' needs before your own.

   How are you doing with your emotional boundaries? (1–5) _____

   Does anything need to change about this boundary? If so, what? _____

   _____

   _____

2. **Physical boundaries** refer to your personal space, your body, and your privacy. These, like all boundaries, vary—some people hug to greet one another, some partners may kiss or hold hands in public, and other people need their own personal space when around others. Knowing and sharing what you do and don't feel comfortable with is important in developing healthy relationships in all areas of life.

   How are you doing with your physical boundaries? (1–5) _____

   Does anything need to change about this boundary? If so, what? _____

   _____

   _____

3. **Mental boundaries** involve respecting your (and others') beliefs, opinions, values, and ideas. When you disregard another person's opinion or talk down to them as though they are not smart, it can affect their self-esteem. When you have healthy mental boundaries, everyone can share their opinions safely and honestly.

How are you doing with your mental boundaries? (1–5) _____

Does anything need to change about this boundary? If so, what? _____

_____

_____

4. **Sexual boundaries** involve the limits you set in intimate relationships, which can include anything from sexual comments to sexual touch. Healthy sexual boundaries should involve consent from both people. In addition, your sexual boundaries are your decision; it's not something you have to compromise on.

How are you doing with your sexual boundaries? (1–5) _____

Does anything need to change about this boundary? If so, what? _____

_____

_____

5. **Financial boundaries** include the limits that you set for your money, including how comfortable you are loaning money to others or always being the friend who buys things for others. When you have poor financial boundaries, it can lead to strained relationships and make you feel taken advantage of, so determining your boundaries early on can support clear expectations and healthy relationships.

How are you doing with your financial boundaries? (1–5) _____

Does anything need to change about this boundary? If so, what? _____

_____

_____

Red Light, Green Light

Learning about healthy boundaries is an important part of growing up. In the spaces beneath each traffic light, write down examples of boundaries that are unsafe (red light), that you are not sure about (yellow light), or that are safe (green light). Then talk to a trusted adult about how these boundaries may change depending on the person, environment, or situation. Some examples have been provided for you.

Red Light	Yellow Light	Green Light
Someone asks me to keep secrets.	A stranger stands close to me.	Someone I trust gives me a wanted hug.

Broken Glass

Like glass, trust can be easily broken. When this happens, it's often difficult to repair or "put back together" what has been broken. Use the following pieces of glass to write or draw about situations, people, or experiences that have led to your trust being broken. For example, perhaps a friend told one of your secrets, your mom lied to you, or someone talked about you behind your back.

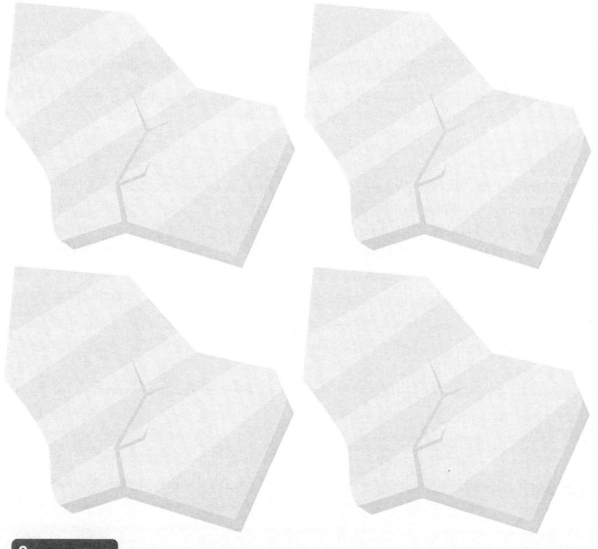

QUESTIONS

- How do you feel when your trust has been broken?
- Has anyone helped rebuild your trust once it was broken? If so, how?
- Have you ever broken someone else's trust? Explain what happened.

Apologies

Although it can be hard to apologize sometimes, saying you're sorry is the first step in repairing a broken relationship. Here are the steps to making an apology:

- Acknowledge the other person's hurt feelings. For example, "I understand you felt hurt."

- Express you're sorry by saying "I am sorry" to the person. Don't make excuses.

- Express what you regret or you wish you would've done differently.

- Take responsibility for what you did. Own your actions.

- Offer an apology by describing what you are willing to do to repair the relationship.

- Let the other person know that you will act differently next time. For example, "I will work harder to speak more calmly when I am angry."

- Keep your focus on the person you've hurt. Don't make it about yourself or blame others.

With these aspects of an apology in hand, use the following space to write out an apology for someone you've hurt recently:

The Puzzle Pieces of Trust

Being trustworthy can mean a lot of different things. What is it about someone that makes you trust them? What do they *do* or *say* that lets you know they are there for you? For example, maybe they keep their promises, or they're always willing to give a listening ear. Think about someone you trust. In each of the following puzzle pieces, write down a piece of trust that lets you know this person is someone you can open up to.

EXPERIENTIAL USE

Label the pieces of an actual jigsaw puzzle with a loved one's trustworthy actions as you put the set together. Or, you can try to create your own puzzle with paper, felt, or any other art materials!

Building an Army

This worksheet will help you consider all the important and helpful people in your life. In each of the following figures, write down a different member of your "army"—these are the supportive people in your life who lift you up, provide you with encouragement, and cheer you on. Explain why you chose each person and describe how they help you reach your goals. For example, you might pick your teacher because she helps you learn new information and makes you feel safe, or you might pick your best friend who is always there for you no matter what.

Ages 13+

Relationship Red Flags

Relationship red flags are warning signs that a relationship you are in may not be healthy. Sometimes these flags might not feel like a big deal in the moment or in comparison with the relationship as a whole; for this reason, you might even be tempted to ignore them. It can be hard to realize when you are in an unhealthy relationship with someone you love or really care about. Read the following statements and check off any red flags you have noticed in your relationship. While these statements focus on romantic relationships, you can apply them to any other relationships in your life as well.

☐ Your partner makes comments that affect how you feel about yourself (e.g., name calling, criticizing, embarrassing you).

☐ Your partner ignores you or gives you the silent treatment.

☐ Your partner pushes, trips, hits, shoves, kicks, or bites you.

☐ You feel blamed for your partner's mistakes.

☐ You feel limited by what you can wear, whom you can see, and what activities you can do.

☐ You feel alone in your relationship.

☐ You feel pressured to engage in activities that you do not want to (e.g., sex, substance use, rough play).

☐ Your partner destroys or damages your property (e.g., breaking or throwing things, ruining pictures, letters, clothing, or gifts).

☐ You feel scared by the way your partner looks, acts, or talks to you.

☐ You feel like you are not in charge of your own decisions.

QUESTIONS

- What did you notice as you went through the checklist?
- Is there anything that stands out to you that you were not aware of before?
- If you have concerns about the health or safety of your relationship, is there someone safe you can speak to?
- Are there any questions you have after completing this worksheet?

Important Resources to Remember!

If you or someone you know needs access to resources or support, please use the following resources or speak with a trusted individual. Save these numbers in your phone so you have them for whenever you may need support.

National Domestic Violence Hotline	www.thehotline.org	1-800-799-SAFE (7233)
National Teen Dating Abuse Helpline	www.loveisrespect.org	1-866-331-9474
National Sexual Assault Hotline	www.rainn.org	1-800-656-HOPE (4673)
988 Suicide and Crisis Lifeline	www.988lifeline.org	1-800-273-TALK (8255) or 988
National Center for Victims of Crime	www.victimsofcrime.org	1-202-467-8700

What Role Do You Play?

The following checklist includes the different roles you may have with friends, with family, at school, and in other relationships. Read through each of the different categories and check the roles that apply to you. If there is a role you take on that is not listed, write it in the blank spaces provided. When you're done, talk with a trusted adult about the roles you identified.

School:

☐ Perfect

☐ Funny

☐ Struggling

☐ Promiscuous

☐ Popular

☐ Other: _____

Family:

☐ Caretaker

☐ Peacemaker

☐ Parent

☐ Scapegoat or "black sheep"

☐ Hero

☐ Truth-teller

☐ Thinker

☐ Other: _____

Social Life:

☐ Leader

☐ Follower

☐ Observer

☐ Smart one

☐ Connector ("glue" of the group)

☐ Always doing what is "right"

☐ Enforcer (the "mom" of the group)

☐ Protector

☐ Other: _____

Solar System

You are the center of your "solar system"—which is the system of friendships and relationships around you! Everyone in your life plays a role in your solar system. Think about all the important people in your life and write them in the following box. Don't forget to include people like your teachers, coaches, neighbors, babysitters, and so on.

Now think about the people you listed in the box. Some of these people are closer to you than others. Looking at the list, place each person inside your solar system, remembering that you are the sun. This means that the names you place farthest from the middle are your less close or important relationships, while the names closest to the middle indicate your tightest relationships—the most important people in your life.

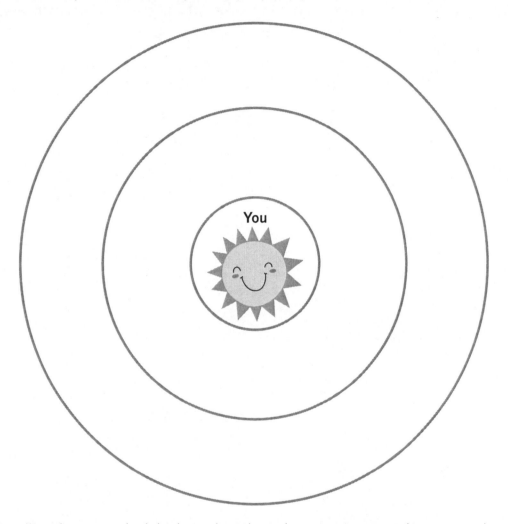

Next, talk with a trusted adult about the role each person in your solar system plays in your life, how close or far they are to you, and how you'd like your solar system to change or stay the same.

EXPERIENTIAL USE

Use yarn or string to represent the rings around your solar system. Then stand in different spots around the room and describe to a trusted adult the role that others play in your life (e.g., "My mom would be here and my teacher would be here").

In Their Eyes

Part of building healthy relationships is being able to put yourself in other people's shoes so you can understand how they may be feeling. This is called having *empathy*. When you have empathy, you can better understand what the other person might need in that moment. Complete the following table to identify what another person might be feeling in each situation, and then come up with an empathetic response that shows that you understand what they are going through. An example has been provided for you first.

Situation	How Do You Think They Feel?	Empathetic Response
Jessie didn't get the grade she wanted on a test she studied for.	Disappointed, sad	"That test was hard, and you did the best you could."
Someone laughed at Antonio when he got a problem wrong.		
Michelle's cat ran away last night.		
Gabriella's stomach hurts.		
Ray got a new toy that he's been asking for.		
Haruki's parents are getting divorced.		

Empathy Crashers

Sometimes, when we see that someone we care about is hurting, we immediately go into problem-solving mode. However, a lot of the time, people don't want someone else to fix their problem. They just want someone to listen to them and to show that they care. This worksheet will help you identify "empathy crashers"—actions to avoid when trying to be empathetic. Read through each of the empathy crashers and identify how you could respond in an empathetic way instead.

Empathy Crasher	Instead of:	Try:	Ready, Set, Go!
You have a group of friends, who are your go-to people. Omar shares with you that he heard Penny was talking about him behind his back. Omar feels embarrassed, angry, and ashamed. You respond by trying to solve the problem so all of you can be friends again.	Solving the problem	Asking them for what they need	
Your friend Teddy opens up about their parents' divorce, stating they are confused, sad, and hurt. Your friend feels hopeless about their future and the unknown. You respond by talking about how great it is to have two households and sharing your feelings related to the news of their parents' divorce.	Offering unwanted advice	Saying "That must be hard, I can't even imagine . . ."	

Empathy Crasher	Instead of:	Try:	Ready, Set, Go!
Your best friend Zach plays soccer. He's had a good season so far, until this last game, which ultimately resulted in the team not making the playoffs. Zach tells you he didn't do a good job and feels that he failed the team. He shares that he is disappointed, angry, embarrassed, and sad. You respond by stating "better luck next season."	Dismissing feelings	Listening and acknowledging their feelings	
You are in class and notice the teacher picking on your friend, Kyra, regarding her reading skills. You are aware that she has trouble reading. After class, you touch base with Kyra and acknowledge what the teacher did by making a joke to make light of the situation.	Making a joke	Being direct and acknowledging the issue	

Suits of Armor

When other people hurt you, you may act in ways to protect yourself, just like a knight wears a suit of armor. For example, you might stop hanging out with the person who hurt you or no longer share your secrets with them, both of which can prevent you from getting hurt again. However, wearing a suit of armor *all* the time can leave you feeling alone and disconnected from others. In order to feel connected, it can be helpful to take off parts of your armor around safe people whom you trust.

On the pieces of your first suit of armor, describe what this armor protects you from. What people, situations, difficult feelings, or experiences does your armor keep you safe from? An example has been provided for you first.

Protects me from . . .

Bullying

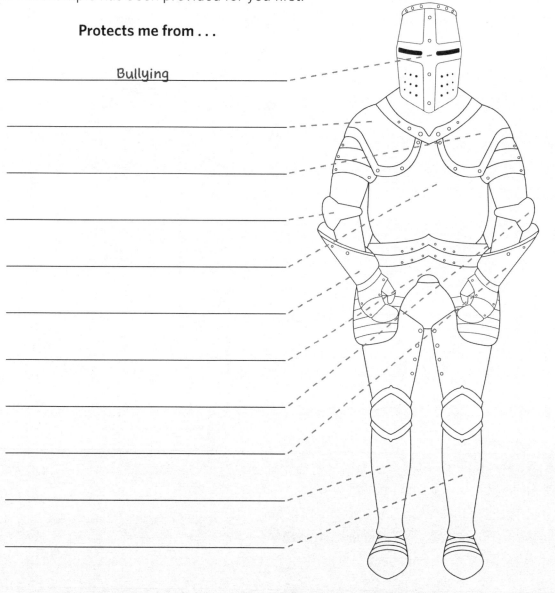

Now, think about taking off your suit of armor. On each of the pieces, write down ways that taking off the suit can be helpful.

Opens me up to . . .

_____ Making friends _____

_____

_____

_____

_____

_____

_____

_____

_____

_____

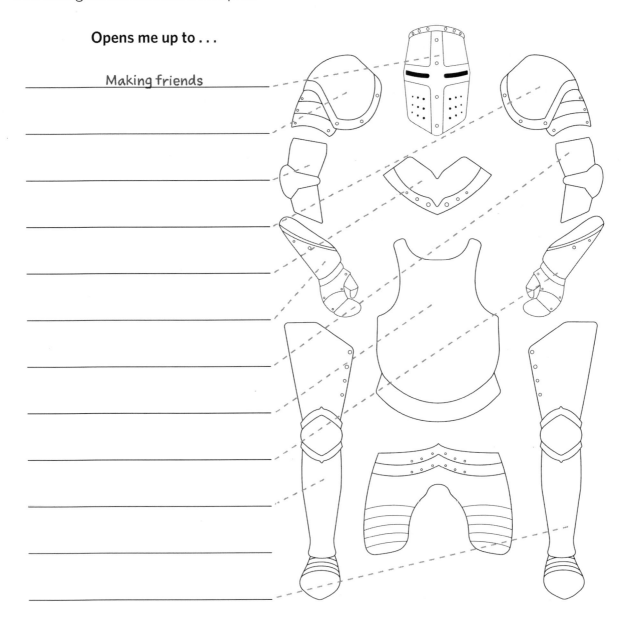

QUESTIONS

- What is your suit of armor protecting you from the most?
- What is the biggest thing your armor is keeping you from experiencing?
- How can others help you to remove your armor?
- What is the scariest part about removing parts of your armor? The most exciting?

Ages
13+

Reality Check

In relationships, you might sometimes confuse what you *want* with what you *need*. A *need* is something that is necessary for you, whereas a *want* is something you hope for or would like to have but isn't necessary. For example, you might want to be friends with someone who owns all the latest video games, but this isn't a reason you *need* to be friends with them. Use the following checklist to identify your needs and wants in relationships.

	Need	Want		Need	Want
Affection			Money		
Attention			Popularity		
Understanding			Laughter		
Trust			Respect		
Chemistry			Getting along		
Common interests			Connection		
Same values			Forgiveness		
Gifts			Physical attraction		
Happiness			Acceptance		
Support			Time spent together		

QUESTIONS

- What makes it hard to share your needs in a relationship?
- What might happen if you don't get what you need in a relationship?
- How could focusing more on wants versus needs affect a relationship?
- How do you find out others' wants and needs, and why is it important?

SECTION 8

Your Body and Your Sexuality

Sometimes, it can be challenging or awkward for adults to have conversations with children and adolescents about their bodies and sex. Not only are kids' bodies growing and changing, but so is the information on physical and sexual development. How you approach and teach these topics can make a significant difference in your relationships with them, as well as how they function in relationships throughout their development. Therefore, this section includes several activities to teach kids about both physical and sexual development, help them maintain physical and sexual boundaries, and provide psychoeducation that debunks myths related to sex, puberty, and all things body related. Topics pertaining to gender identity, body image, and consent are included as well. There are also activities that provide a space and structure for kids to ask the tough questions they may not feel comfortable talking to adults about.

The most important thing to remember about the topics of sex, physical development, and sexuality is that if you don't talk to kids about this, they will find out the information from somewhere else. They may do their own research online, ask friends, or engage in risky or exploratory behaviors to get their own answers. By using the tools in this section, you can have conversations that are appropriate for various ages and stages of development. From learning the basics about body parts and safe body boundaries, to exploring sexual orientation and the basics of safe sex, we have included helpful information to allow you to better navigate these challenging but increasingly important topics. The more kids know, the better they do!

I Was Wondering . . .

We learn about our bodies in lots of different ways—from our families or friends, at school, or sometimes by things that happen to us. The following list includes some common questions that kids and adolescents have about their developing bodies. Read through the questions and check off any that you may have. If you have other questions, write them in the blank spaces. Then talk about these questions with a trusted adult who you believe will answer them honestly and without judgment.

☐ Is it normal for everyone's bodies to develop at different times?

☐ What is masturbation?

☐ What are the anatomical or scientific names of all the private parts?

☐ Where are all the different places I will grow hair on my body?

☐ How will my body shape change when I go through puberty?

☐ Is it normal that I am thinking about having sex?

☐ How might my skin change when I go through puberty?

☐ Is it normal that different body parts are starting to smell?

☐ Is it normal for my emotions to feel all over the place?

☐ Is it normal to feel sexually or physically attracted to others?

☐ What is vaginal or penile discharge, and what does it mean?

☐ When, what, and how should I shave?

☐ When is it appropriate for me to have sex?

☐ _____

☐ _____

☐ _____

☐ _____

☐ _____

Ages 7+

Body Basics

We all learn about our bodies in different ways, including from our parents, siblings, or peers. The same goes for messages about how our bodies "should" look or what we can and cannot do with them. In the following body outline, write or draw all the body parts you know, including private parts. After labeling the body, feel free to add in anything you've heard regarding the different body parts or thoughts you have about your own.

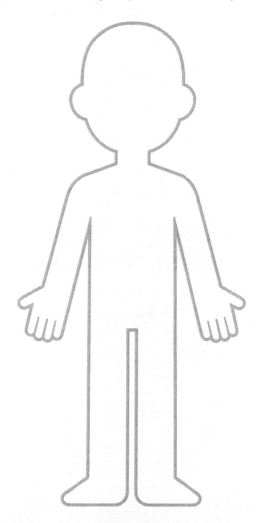

QUESTIONS

- Who taught you the names of all the body parts? When did you learn this?
- How do you feel about your body?
- What messages have others sent you about your body?
- Is there anything confusing about your body or bodies in general?
- What are three things you love about your body (and what it can do for you)?

Basic Body Boundaries

Now that you've labeled all the parts of your body, let's talk about boundaries for each part. Think about how you labeled your body in the *Body Basics* worksheet. In the following stop signs, write down the boundaries you have for each part of your body. An example has been provided for you first. Remember that your boundaries may change depending on the people you are with or the situation you are in.

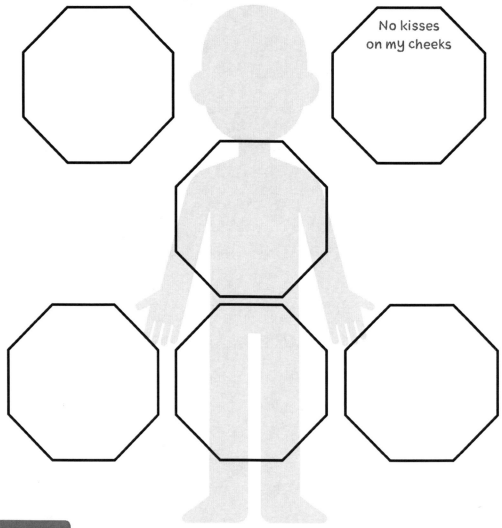

No kisses
on my cheeks

QUESTIONS

- How do your body boundaries change? For example, do they change with certain people or in certain situations (e.g., at the doctor's office)?
- How did you learn what your body boundaries are?
- What would you do if someone crossed your body boundaries?

Hula Hoop

One of the most important ways you can set boundaries about your body is to learn about personal space. Personal space is a boundary that changes based on the person, situation, or how you feel. Use the following picture to imagine yourself using a hula hoop! Depending on the situation, you may want your hula hoop to be bigger (to keep *more* space between you and other people) or smaller (to have *less* space between you and other people). Read through each of the questions and draw hula hoops of different sizes to represent the boundaries you would have depending on the person, situation, or how you're feeling.

People
How much space do you need with:
- Family (separate hula hoops for each member of your family)?
- Friends?
- Strangers?
- Teachers?
- Coaches?
- Doctors?

Situations
How much space do you need when you're:
- Playing a sport with your friends?
- At a party where you don't know many people?
- On a date with someone you just met?
- At an extended family member's house for a holiday visit?
- Getting a checkup at the doctor's office?

Feelings
How much space do you need when you feel:
- Angry?
- Excited?
- Sad?
- Worried?
- Confident?

QUESTIONS

- How do you communicate your personal space to others?
- What can you do if someone doesn't respect your personal space?
- Can you think of any other situations, people, or feelings that would change the size of your hula hoop?

Ages 12+

Consent Ladder

Consent is an essential part of boundaries, especially in intimate relationships and sexual experiences. Consent is giving permission and being able to say no in *any* situation. Next to each step on the ladder, write down what that step of consent means to you. Remember, all parties need *every* step to have true consent, so if you miss a step, you'll fall off the ladder—which means you, or someone else, has overstepped a boundary. When you're done, compare your definitions to the information on the next page to learn more about the steps of consent.

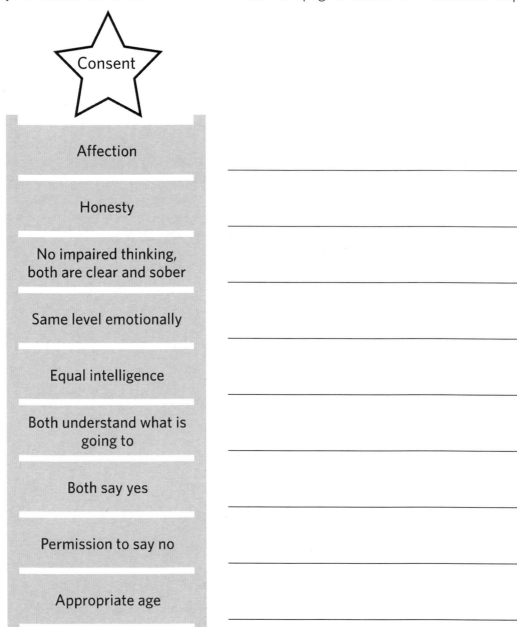

Consent

Affection

_____

Honesty

_____

No impaired thinking, both are clear and sober

_____

Same level emotionally

_____

Equal intelligence

_____

Both understand what is going to

_____

Both say yes

_____

Permission to say no

_____

Appropriate age

_____

Steps of Consent

Appropriate age:

- The legal age of consent is 17 in many states (check your state's specific laws).

- A person may be a certain age but have mental limitations that prevent them from giving consent.

- Think about your friend group: What would you think if a high school student was hanging out with an elementary school student?

- The rule of thumb is your partner should be no more than two years younger or older than you.

Permission to say no:

- The relationship should feel safe, meaning that you're comfortable expressing your feelings, sharing your beliefs, and being yourself.

- You are given the option to say no and your decision is respected.

- No means no!

- If you change your mind at any point (from a yes to a no), that is okay!

- No one pressures you to say yes or makes you feel guilty for saying no.

Both say yes:

- Both partners understand and agree to have sex.

- Both partners want the same thing.

- Both partners give permission.

Both understand what is going to happen:

- There is an open discussion of sex where you talk about expectations and define what will happen.

- Be sure the other person understands your expectations and you understand theirs.

- You talk about it *before* it happens. Sex doesn't just happen!

Equal intelligence:

- Both partners have the same education and awareness about sex.

- Both partners understand the basics of sex.

- Neither person should have any developmental delays, meaning that both their brains function at the same level.

Same level emotionally:

- Both partners have the same maturity level and the same beliefs and attitudes about sex.

- Both partners feel ready to have sex.

- Sex brings up a lot of feelings that can be confusing, and everyone experiences and manages emotions differently. You and your partner should both be able to manage emotions in a healthy way.

No impaired thinking, both are clear and sober:

- Be careful with alcohol, drugs, or other substances that can impair your decision-making before or during sex (e.g., foggy thinking, difficulty controlling your body).

- You know whether the other person has used substances (and if so, how much) before you decide to have sex.

- Both partners know what is going on in their environment. If you wouldn't be able to drive a car safely, you cannot consent to sex!

Honesty:

- Both partners tell the truth—no lying about who you are, how old you are, what you want to do, your health, or your previous sexual experience.

- You are open about what you want with each other.

Affection:

- You care about each other.

- You like and trust each other.

- You can be yourself with each other.

Body Image

Ages 12+

The way you see your body can be shaped by how you think you look, the things other people say about your body, and even what you have seen on social media, in the movies, or in music lyrics. This worksheet will help you explore four different types of body image: **perceptual** (the way you see yourself), **affective** (the way you feel about how you look), **cognitive** (thoughts you have about your body), and **behavioral** (things you do because of the way you look). On the following bodies, write or draw your body image in each of these areas.

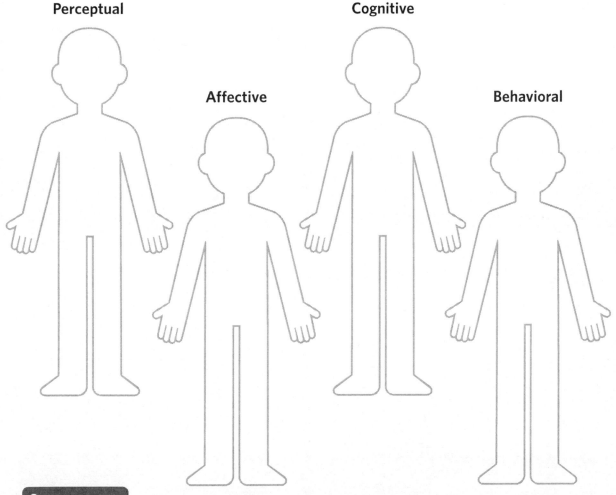

Perceptual

Affective

Cognitive

Behavioral

QUESTIONS

- Do you think the way you see yourself is the same as how other people see you?
- What do you want to think and feel about your body?
- Are the thoughts and feelings you have about your body positive, negative, or both?
- Are the behaviors you identified healthy, unhealthy, or both?

Love the Skin You're In

People often receive so many messages about what their bodies "should" look like or what their bodies "should" be able to do that they don't spend enough time thinking about all the wonderful things their bodies do for them. Inside the heart, write or draw all the qualities you love about your body and explain why. Then think about the body parts you struggle to love and see if you can come up with any ways that they help you. For example, you might not love the shape of your legs, but they do allow you to walk, run, and dance. Write these down on the outside of the frame.

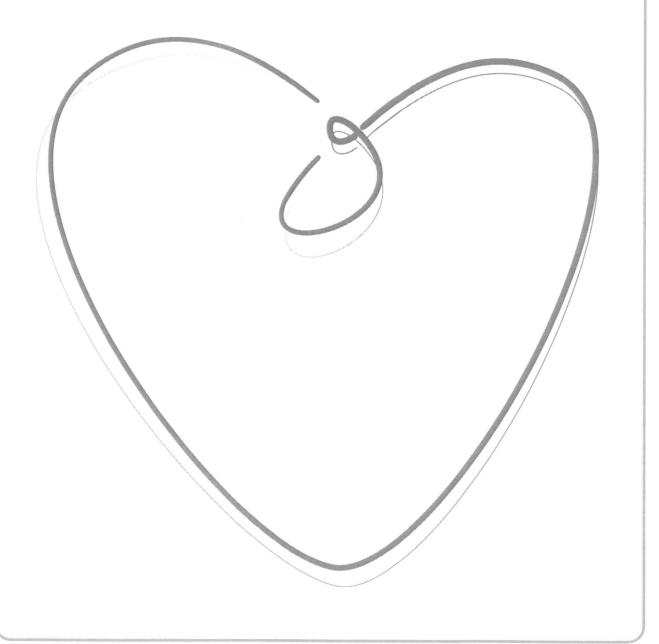

Ages 12+

Myth or Fact

There is so much information we receive about sex and sexuality. Sometimes we learn about these topics at school, from our friends, or online. With all this information swirling out there, it is hard to know what is true versus what is a myth. On the list below, indicate whether you believe each statement about sex or sexuality is true or false. Some of these statements may not be completely true or false, and the answer may depend on your values, beliefs, and opinions about relationships. When you're done, look over the answer key and talk about your responses with a trusted adult to find out the facts and discuss what is important to you!

_____ 1. Everyone is having sex.

_____ 2. You can only get a sexually transmitted infection (STI) if you have vaginal intercourse.

_____ 3. It is normal to be confused about who you are attracted to.

_____ 4. If someone wants to have sex with you, it is okay to say no.

_____ 5. "Pulling out" is a reliable form of birth control.

_____ 6. Any form of penetration is considered sex.

_____ 7. You cannot get pregnant if you have not yet had your first period.

_____ 8. It is wrong to masturbate, regardless if you are male or female.

_____ 9. You can still consent to sex when under the influence of substances.

_____ 10. Birth control cannot protect you from STIs.

_____ 11. If you have sex with a condom, there is no chance you will get pregnant.

_____ 12. If you love someone (or someone loves you), you should have sex with them.

_____ 13. You must make a decision to have sex with either males or females.

_____ 14. You do not have to be in a relationship to have sex.

_____ 15. If someone asks for an explicit photo (over social media), you have the right to say no.

_____ 16. If you say no to sex, people will think you're weird.

Answer Key

1. **False:** There are many people who decide not to have sex until they are older or until they feel ready. There are also people that may be having sex but are not sharing that information with others. While it may seem like everyone is talking about sex or who they are "hooking up" with, only you can decide when the right time is for you to have sex and with whom.

2. **False:** There are numerous ways to get an STI, and it's not only from intercourse. Oral sex, anal sex, and skin-to-skin contact are other common ways infections and diseases are passed from person to person.

3. **True:** Typically, sexual feelings and feelings of attraction toward other people come up around puberty. During this time of development, it is common for a person to feel attracted to both sexes and varying genders, or even to have confusion about their sexuality in general. This is normal, and it can be helpful to discuss with an adult who you trust.

4. **True:** It is okay to say no if someone wants to have sex and you decide you do not want to. It is *not* okay if someone pressures or tries to talk you into having sex. You can say no to sex—and to *any* kind of sexual interaction—without giving a reason; the person asking should be understanding and accepting. What are some situations where it might be difficult or complicated for you to say no when you do not want to have sex?

5. **False:** "Pulling out," or removing the penis from the vagina before ejaculation, is not a reliable form of birth control. This is because the penis creates pre-ejaculate, which contains sperm that enter into the vagina during sex and can cause pregnancy.

6. **True:** Any time a penis enters any opening in the body, it can be considered sex. For instance, oral and anal penetration are still considered sex. Even if the penis does not fully enter the opening, it is still considered sex.

7. **False:** When a young woman begins her menstrual cycle, or period, her body releases an egg from her ovary, a process called ovulation. This egg can be fertilized by a male sperm, resulting in pregnancy. However, ovulation can happen prior to your first menstrual cycle, so it is still possible to get pregnant even if you have not yet had your period.

8. **False:** Masturbation is a very normal part of sexual development. It is common for us as humans to discover our bodies and masturbate because it is pleasurable, or feels good. Even babies play with their private parts to self-soothe.

9. **False:** When either or both people are under the influences of substances, it is usually not appropriate to determine consent. This is especially true if either or both people are in an altered state of mind (e.g., drunk, high). Consent is most safely determined by people who are sober or under minimal

influence of substances (i.e., not impaired). A good rule of thumb is that if you would not be able to drive a car, you are not able to give consent for sex.

10. **True:** Birth control prevents pregnancy, but it cannot protect you from sexually transmitted infections. Only condoms (both male and female) and abstinence can protect against STIs, and abstinence is the only way to ensure complete protection against STIs. Skin-to-skin contact (without any sexual intercourse) can also be a risk for contracting an STI.

11. **False:** Wearing a condom during sex is a highly reliable way to prevent pregnancy, but several issues can decrease the condom's effectiveness, including it breaking, being expired, or being worn incorrectly. In these situations, pregnancy may occur. Even when worn perfectly, condoms do not prevent against pregnancy 100 percent of the time.

12. **False:** When two people love each other, they may decide to have sex, but one or both of these people may also decide not to, which is completely okay. Loving someone does not mean you should, or even want to, have sex with them. People in loving relationships respect each other's boundaries and don't pressure the other person into having sex. (For any questions on boundaries, see section 7.) There are many other ways to show love, both physically and emotionally. What are some ways you can show love to someone other than sex?

13. **False:** It is common to be attracted to both males and females. When it comes to the decision to have sex, it is most important that you do so in the context of a healthy, supportive relationship where everyone's boundaries are respected. Some people decide to have sex with only those who identify as male or those who identify as female, and some people decide to have sex with both.

14. **True:** This one can be tricky! It is true that you may decide to have sex without being in a traditional relationship or marriage. While this is neither right nor wrong, it is helpful to have some type of supportive relationship with someone prior to having sex with them. This could be a friendship, for instance. Again, it is most important that the person you are choosing to have sex with respects your boundaries and that the sex is consensual. Ultimately, you decide what you do with your body. It's your choice!

15. **True:** You *always* have the right to say no when it comes to any form of sexual interaction. Sending explicit photos of any kind, whether over social media, text, or email, can put you at risk of being exploited, meaning that other people whom you do *not* want to see these photos could receive them. Can you think of other reasons sending explicit photos could be risky? Also, being underage and sending or receiving sexually explicit pictures can be a crime, depending on federal and state laws.

16. **False:** Remember, you can *always* say no to sex. Everyone has different opinions, but it is important to make the choice that is right for you. There are many people who decide not to have sex for many different reasons. Any reason not to have sex is valid and should not change how your friends or partner feel about you.

Changing the Conversation:
Treatment Provider Edition

Talking about sex with clients has its challenges. However, it is important to remember that sex education is about *exploring* and *teaching*. Remember to not allow your own biases and beliefs to impact the conversation. If this is a difficult topic of conversation for you, we encourage you to seek further training and support to enhance your understanding and level of comfort talking about sex. Here are some tips for navigating these important but challenging conversations:

- Acknowledge and become aware of your own biases, beliefs, and perspective. Remember that this is about your client and providing a space to assist them to explore sex and sexuality.

- Respect the family's belief system while also providing psychoeducation and factual information.

- Normalize this important aspect of development.

- Do not judge! Passing judgment is the worst thing you can do.

- Have fun, laugh, and acknowledge the discomfort.

- Validate each individual's beliefs and perspective, even if they differ from your own or you do not agree!

Changing the Conversation: Adolescent Edition

As an adolescent, it might be hard to ask questions about sex for many reasons, such as embarrassment, fear of judgment, or awkwardness. Although you may turn to outside sources for this information, like friends or social media, these are often not the most accurate or reliable sources of information. Instead, use the following table to think of any specific questions or voice any specific concerns you have about sexual behavior. When you are done, use your completed worksheet to have a conversation with a trusted adult.

	Questions	Concerns
Sexuality		
Sex		
Consent		
Birth control		
Pregnancy		
Sexually transmitted infections		

Changing the Conversation:
Trusted Adult Edition

As a trusted adult, it can be uncomfortable to answer your child's questions related to sex and sexuality. It's hard to imagine that your child is thinking about, curious about, or even interested in sex! However, *you* are the most valuable and accurate source of information, as opposed to information that your child may hear from friends or on social media. Your child has completed a previous worksheet where they have asked questions and voiced concerns about sexuality, sex, consent, birth control, pregnancy, and STIs. Before you go over the worksheet with them, answer the following questions so you can best prepare yourself to have a discussion with them and address any fears or concerns they might have. Remember, sex is a totally normal, healthy, and natural part of development.

What is the most important message you want to share with your child about sex and sexuality?

_____

_____

_____

What do you fear will happen if your child learns more about these topics? Are these fears related to you or your child?

_____

_____

_____

What are your expectations for your child as they begin navigating their sexuality? What decisions do you hope they will make regarding sex?

_____

_____

_____

How can you meet your child where they are and support them in this aspect of their development?

_____

_____

_____

How do you want your child to feel as they have this important yet challenging conversation with you?

_____

_____

_____

Ages 12+

Sexuality and Me

Your sexuality is a part of who you are, so it's only natural that it can affect your thoughts, feelings, relationships, and life experiences. Sexuality includes physical attraction (e.g., whom you want to kiss) and romantic attraction (e.g., whose hand you would want to hold at the movies). Answer the following questions about your sexuality. When you are finished, use your answers to process this information with a trusted adult.

What is your sexuality like? How does it impact you and who you are as a person?

_____

_____

_____

_____

What do other people think about your sexuality? How do you know this?

_____

_____

_____

_____

What gender(s) do you identify with? How does this impact you and who you are as a person?

_____

_____

_____

_____

Think about the last time you were in a relationship. What was it like? How did it make you feel?

_____

_____

_____

_____

Do you experience any conflicts between who you are and who others tell you to be? If so, describe them here.

_____

_____

_____

_____

L, G, B, T, or Q . . . Be True to You!

As you begin to figure out who you are as a person, society can have its own expectations and norms that make you question who you are. This can be really hard, but we want you to know that you are not alone! To help you figure out who you are and be true to yourself, read through the following list of sexualities and see if there are any that you can relate with at this time. It may be one, or it may be several! Please note that this list is not inclusive but a broad overview.

Asexual:	Having little or no sexual attraction to others, or little to no desire for sexual activity
Demisexual:	Only feeling sexually attracted to someone when you have an emotional bond with that person
Pansexual:	Being attracted to people of all genders
Bisexual:	Being sexually attracted to more than one gender
Gay or lesbian:	Being sexually attracted to people of the same sex
Heterosexual:	Being sexually attracted to people of the opposite sex (also called being "straight")

QUESTIONS

- Where do you think you fall on this spectrum? If you don't know, that's okay!
- Do you feel like you can be true to who you are? If not, what makes it difficult to be true to who you are, and what would help you be more comfortable with who you truly are?
- Is there anything you are currently questioning about your sexuality?
- What thoughts or feelings come up when discussing your sexuality?
- Who has provided you information on your sexuality?
- What do you need from others to feel supported? Who can provide this?
- What do you need from yourself to feel supported?

Important Resources to Remember!

If you or someone you know needs access to resources or support, please use the following resources or speak with a trusted individual. Save these numbers in your phone so you have them for whenever you may need support.

The Trevor Project	www.thetrevorproject.org	1-866-488-7386
It Gets Better	www.itgetsbetter.org	N/A
GLAAD	www.glaad.org	N/A
PFLAG	https://pflag.org	N/A

SECTION 9

Self-Esteem and Respect

Helping kids build healthy self-esteem takes practice and work, especially when they struggle with self-criticism. To help kids overcome these negative thoughts and boost their self-confidence, this section contains a variety of tools to help kids identify their positive attributes and develop gratitude for what they have in life. Although kids might feel that focusing on their strengths and accomplishments is selfish, it is important to remember that self-love is not selfish. In fact, it is only once kids believe in themselves that they can start achieving what they never thought possible. In addition, when kids know who they are and what they believe in, they are better able to make tough decisions, maintain healthy relationships, and stay motivated.

Finally, in order for kids to develop healthy self-esteem, it is important for them to learn how to respect themselves and others. Since respect is not always given—it is earned—the tools in this section will help kids learn what it means to honor themselves and others with dignity and worth. Respect doesn't mean proving that you're older, wiser, or "right." Rather, it's about validating and accepting people for who they are. The activities in this section will help kids learn how to do just that.

What Character Are You?

Have you ever thought about what character you would be if you were in a comic book, cartoon, or movie? Identify which character you picture yourself being. If you can't think of a character, feel free to create your own! Then, in the comic bubbles, identify the positive qualities this character has that you also see in yourself.

Character name: _____

EXPERIENTIAL USE

Draw, act out, or dress up as the character you see yourself to be. Think about the qualities you see in this character and how these relate to the qualities you see in yourself.

QUESTIONS

- How is the character you chose the same or different from you? In what ways?
- Is there anything you would like to change about yourself or the character you chose? If so, why?
- What are some good things you want to remember about yourself?

Gratitude Bucket

Fill up the bucket by writing or drawing all the objects, thoughts, experiences, people, or emotions you are grateful for. Even the smallest of smallest smiles count. Think hard. This one is for you!

EXPERIENTIAL USE

Identify various objects (e.g., figurines, toys, action figures—be creative!) that represent items you are grateful for and place these items in a bucket. As you place each item in, discuss the experience with a trusted adult.

Pop Those Thoughts

Negative self-talk refers to any thoughts that bring you down or make you feel bad about yourself. In the following bubbles, write down any negative self-talk that you struggle with. Then imagine popping those thoughts and watching them disappear! As the thoughts fade, write down some more positive and helpful things you could say to yourself in the rainbow.

Blow actual bubbles and imagine that each bubble contains one of your negative thoughts. Then pop these bubbles and watch them disappear from the air!

Give to Get

Have you ever had the thought: "They don't respect me, so why should I respect them?" It is important to remember that both people in a relationship are equally responsible for showing respect to one another. You have to give respect to get respect. This is true no matter the ups and downs that naturally happen in a relationship. Think about what *respect* means to you. Then use the following boxes to describe how you would most like to receive—and give—respect. Use the actions provided in the word bank or come up with your own!

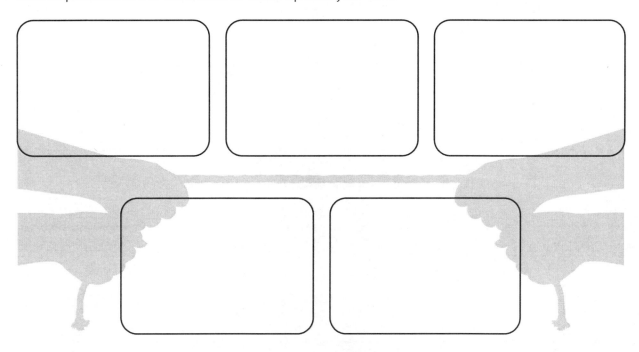

Listening	Validating others	Being patient	Not judging
Talking kindly	Feeling heard	Compromising	Giving compliments
Being honest	Not being distracted	Making eye contact	Being grateful
Apologizing when you're wrong		Taking responsibility for your actions	

QUESTIONS

- Who has disrespected you in the past? Is there anyone you've disrespected?
- Why is it hard to give respect and not get any respect in return?
- What makes it hard for you to give respect to others?
- What are some ways you respect yourself even if others do not show you the same kind of respect?

R-E-S-P-E-C-T

We all have our own definition of respect, and sometimes this can get lost when communicating with others. Use this worksheet to define what respect means to you. Get creative! Come up with your own definition of respect by using song lyrics, famous quotes, your own thoughts, or anything else that comes to mind. Since it is important to communicate not only what respect means to you, but also what it means to others, make several copies of this sheet so you can share your answers with others and give them an opportunity to fill it out as well.

When I think of respect, I _____

_____.

I feel respected when _____

_____.

I show respect by _____

_____.

Someone disrespects me by _____

_____.

Respect means _____

_____.

I learned about respect from _____

_____.

The person I respect the most is _____

_____.

Things that make it hard to show respect are _____

_____.

Your Feed versus Your Reality

The person you show to the world is not always who you truly are on the inside. For example, you may pretend that your life is perfect on social media, when in reality, you carry a lot of pain and shame. In the left column, describe or draw the different ways you present yourself to the world. Then, in the right column, describe or draw who you *truly* are (the good, the bad, and the ugly).

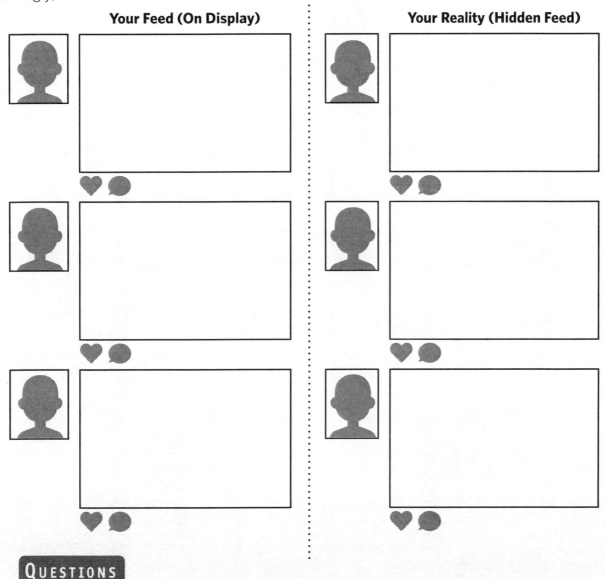

QUESTIONS

- What do you notice about your two feeds? How are they similar or different?
- Which qualities on either feed would you like to change (or keep)?
- What are some things you can do to help your feeds match?

Mirror, Mirror

Let's focus on the positive—your positive qualities, that is! We often spend so much time focused on the things we don't like about ourselves, which negatively affects our thoughts, feelings, and behaviors. This worksheet is designed to help you identify the positive qualities you see in yourself, as well as the positive qualities others see in you. Take some time to think about everything you are good at. For example, maybe you're a good friend, respectful, honest, a hard worker, and funny. List these items on the mirror on the left.

Next, think about any positive qualities others have mentioned when describing you. Feel free to talk to other supportive people in your life to get their input. List these on the mirror on the right. Remember, the more you focus on your positive qualities, the better you'll be able to challenge the negative self-talk and feel better about yourself.

Positive Qualities
I See in Myself

Positive Qualities
Others See in Me

EXPERIENTIAL USE

Create your own "mirrors" for this activity using paper, magazines, and markers. Alternatively, you can look into a real mirror while you identify these positive qualities in yourself.

Stick to Self-Love

When your self-esteem could use a boost, this activity will remind you of all the wonderful, positive qualities you bring to the world. On each of the sticky notes, write one thing you like about yourself. When you are finished, cut them out and put them in various places around your house to remind yourself of how great you are when you are feeling down.

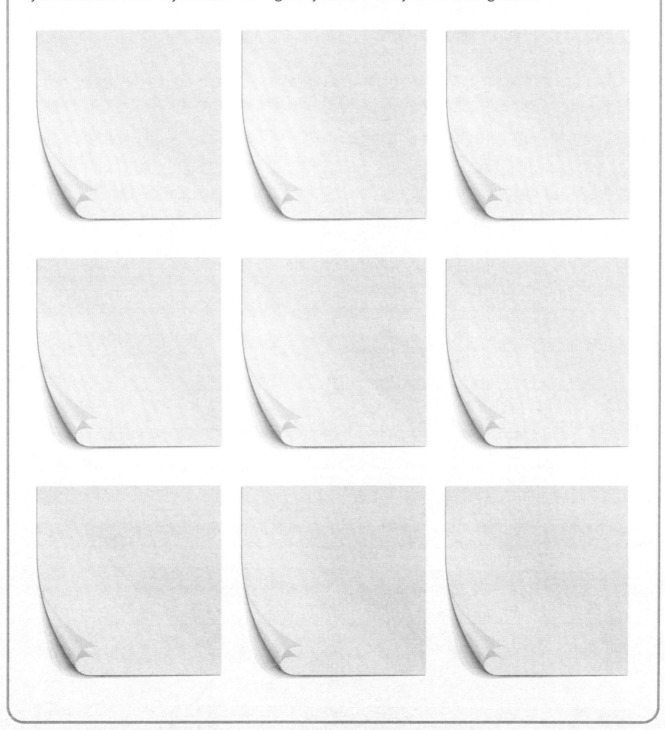

Ring Your Own Bell

While it can feel uplifting to hear positive things about yourself from other people, being able to cheer yourself on can go a long way. Complete the following prompts as best as you can— and watch out for those sneaky judgments and negative thoughts! If you cannot finish every statement, that is okay too. Try to complete as many as possible.

A difficult situation that I have overcome: _____

_____

One thing I am naturally good at: _____

_____

A characteristic of mine that other people compliment me on: _____

_____

Something I have done that I am proud of: _____

_____

A personality trait that makes me feel unique: _____

_____

Positive ways I show others that I care: _____

_____

Something I have worked hard to become good at: _____

_____

Something I am grateful for: _____

_____

Ways that I am a good friend: _____

_____

A value of mine that I am proud of: _____

_____

Something that is meaningful to me: _____

_____

One way that I am creative: _____

_____

A difficult decision I made that I am proud of: _____

_____

One thing that makes me believe in myself: _____

_____

A way that I show myself respect: _____

_____

A time I did the right thing even though it was hard: _____

_____

Something that I like about myself: _____

_____

Something that I enjoy doing on my own: _____

_____

One way I am working to make a difference in the world: _____

_____

Validation versus Invalidation

Validation is about recognizing a person's feelings, thoughts, and experiences. Invalidation involves dismissing someone's feelings or experiences. Validation builds you up, while invalidation tears you down. Read the following statements and circle whether you think the statement is validating or invalidating. Remember, you do not have to agree with someone to validate them!

1.	"You shouldn't feel that way."	**Validation**	**Invalidation**
2.	"It sounds like you had a difficult day."	**Validation**	**Invalidation**
3.	"Stop crying or I'll give you something to cry about."	**Validation**	**Invalidation**
4.	"I'm sorry you're sad."	**Validation**	**Invalidation**
5.	"Your day sucked, but my day was worse than yours."	**Validation**	**Invalidation**
6.	"I don't care if you're mad at me."	**Validation**	**Invalidation**
7.	"You're wrong."	**Validation**	**Invalidation**
8.	"I understand that this is important to you."	**Validation**	**Invalidation**
9.	"It sounds like you're disappointed."	**Validation**	**Invalidation**
10.	"Just let it go and get over it."	**Validation**	**Invalidation**

Here are some other ways people can receive validation. Check off those that are important to you:

☐ When someone looks at me when I am talking and nods along

☐ When someone I trust offers or gives a hug or comforting physical touch

☐ When someone reflects back what I have said to them

☐ When someone works to understand why I feel the way I feel or think the way I think, even if they don't agree with me

☐ When someone treats me as an equal, not less than or incompetent

☐ When someone puts down their phone or stops doing whatever they are doing (not multitasking) and gives me their undivided attention

☐ When someone is genuine in their responses and interactions

☐ When someone is accepting and doesn't judge me

The Art of Self-Validation

When you don't receive validation from others—or worse, when you're invalidated or disrespected—you can practice the art of self-validation by lifting yourself up with positive statements and actions. The following list includes statements and activities you can use to validate yourself. Check off the ones that stand out to you and start practicing!

Statements for Self-Validation:

☐ "I am doing the best I can with what I have."

☐ "Everyone makes mistakes."

☐ "It's okay to feel _____."

☐ "My feelings are valid."

☐ "I like _____ about myself."

☐ "I matter."

☐ "That was _____ (e.g., hard, hurtful, satisfying, scary)."

☐ "My feelings matter, and I will listen to what they are telling me."

☐ Other: _____

Activities for Self-Validation:

☐ Remind yourself of the times you have failed and overcome.

☐ Allow yourself to say no to others, even if you feel guilty about it.

☐ Take a break from social media.

☐ Track your everyday achievements (even the ones you think are small!).

☐ Reward yourself for your achievements.

☐ Hang sticky notes with positive statements around your house wherever you will see them (see the *Stick to Self-Love* activity).

☐ Remind yourself of the qualities you like about yourself.

☐ Practice self-care (e.g., take a hot bath, light a candle, read a book, spend time with a friend).

☐ Other: _____

SECTION 10

Handling Today's Technology, Social Injustices, and Thinking About the Future

Technology—it's every parent's favorite topic of conversation. Everyone has an opinion on how to best navigate kids' digital usage in our ever-changing world. While technology can certainly be helpful, it also has the potential for significant harm, especially with the rise of social media, which highlights both the good and bad in people and of the world. The fact of the matter is social media is now a normal part of adolescent development, so parents must learn how to help children navigate technology and social media in a healthy way. We have included several worksheets and handouts to assist in this process.

With the rise of social media, there has also been increasing awareness of social injustices in the world. While you cannot control or shield children from some of these injustices, you can help them understand how to manage and respond to these experiences. In working through this section, we encourage you to check in with your own biases, as your views may differ from your clients. Create a nonjudgmental space to have these tough conversations and understand that kids have their own experiences and views of the world.

Finally, while the future can be scary, it is important to help kids reflect on where they have been and what they still want to accomplish. Make sure to celebrate their accomplishments and make room for their continued growth. As a therapist, your job is to create the space that allows kids to be their best selves, but it is the child's job to make the decision about where they want to go from here.

Social World

Almost everyone uses some kind of social media. It is available on almost every device! However, social media can be both helpful and harmful. Read through the following actions and indicate whether you believe they are healthy or unhealthy. Then check off any behaviors that apply to your social media usage.

☐ Staying up late or getting up early to use social media **Healthy** **Unhealthy**

☐ Including personal information (e.g., address, school, birthday) in your public profile information **Healthy** **Unhealthy**

☐ Knowing all your followers **Healthy** **Unhealthy**

☐ Bullying or being bullied **Healthy** **Unhealthy**

☐ Having multiple accounts **Healthy** **Unhealthy**

☐ Following people who post positive and healthy messages **Healthy** **Unhealthy**

☐ Following people who post things related to self-harm, unhealthy eating habits, or drug or alcohol use **Healthy** **Unhealthy**

☐ Sharing positive things about your life with people who are important to you **Healthy** **Unhealthy**

☐ Connecting with friends and family who live far away **Healthy** **Unhealthy**

☐ Mindless scrolling **Healthy** **Unhealthy**

QUESTIONS

- How would you describe your relationship with social media? Why?
- What are some consequences of having an unhealthy relationship with social media?
- What do you primarily use social media for?
- When you look to your future, what do you want to look back and see on your social media feed?

Virtual Agreement

Limits regarding internet and social media usage, and screen time in general, is one of the most common reasons that families argue. Sometimes adults set boundaries around screen time that kids don't agree with. To develop clear expectations regarding screen time and compromises that work for everyone, answer the following questions to create a virtual agreement with the trusted adults in your life. You can treat this contract as a living document, meaning that it is flexible and can change depending on specific situations relating to you and your family. This agreement is not a punishment, but a set of boundaries to avoid conflict and inconsistencies.

1. What type of technology can you use (e.g., smart phone, tablet, computer, TV)?

    _____

2. What type of social media can you use (e.g., Snapchat, TikTok, Instagram, Facebook)?

    _____

3. What time should you shut off or turn in your devices on school nights and weeknights?

    _____

4. What does your technology use look like on weekends or holidays?

    _____

5. What does your technology use look like on vacation or during travel times?

    _____

6. Is there a limit on how much screen time you have each day? If so, what is the limit?

    _____

7. There is a time and place for screen time. Our family does not use devices during these times:

    _____ Meals together   _____ Sleepovers

    _____ Family gatherings   _____ While driving

    _____ Family activities (specify which): _____

    _____

8. What expectations do you have for charging devices (e.g., in bedrooms, in common areas)?

_____

_____

_____

_____

9. The use of technology is a privilege, not a right. Devices will not be available after school until you complete your homework and the following chores:

_____ Making beds   _____ Helping prepare dinner

_____ Cleaning up rooms   _____ Other: _____

_____ Doing dishes   _____ Other: _____

_____ Taking care of pets   _____ Other: _____

10. Too much screen time can be unhealthy. What are alternatives to screen time that you can agree to as a family?

_____ Exercise   _____ Reading for pleasure

_____ Sports   _____ Family game night

_____ Musical instruments   _____ Other: _____

_____ Art   _____ Other: _____

_____ Dance   _____ Other: _____

11. Will your family practice password sharing? Discuss and describe how this will be done.

_____

_____

_____

_____

12. No secret accounts or apps will be permitted.

13. Are there any boundaries or limitations to your social media behavior (e.g., pictures posted, names used, bullying, etc.)?

_____

_____

_____

_____

14. What will happen if this virtual agreement is broken?

_____

_____

_____

_____

I agree to this contract. I will discuss any changes or concerns with my family. I understand that using technology is a privilege. I agree to be safe with my technology use.

Date: _____

Signatures:

Signature: _____

Signature: _____

Signature: _____

Signature: _____

Signature: _____

Parenting and Social Media

The world today is very different than it was when you were growing up. Remember when you used to be able to play outside until it was dark? When you got your first cell phone (you know, flip phones)? When you had to learn how to use email? Yup, us too! As much as we hate to admit it, social media is a staple in today's world, especially for growing adolescents. This worksheet will help you examine some myths and facts about social media. Next to each statement, indicate whether you believe it is true or false. When you're done, compare your answers with those in the answer key on the next page.

_____ 1. Social media allows adolescents to socialize.

_____ 2. Social media provides access to beneficial and helpful resources.

_____ 3. You should not have access to your child's account names and passwords.

_____ 4. It's okay to be your child's friend or follower on social media.

_____ 5. You should just let your child do whatever they want on social media.

_____ 6. The threat of child pornography charges is only used as a scare tactic.

_____ 7. There is no danger in social media.

_____ 8. Social media provides a platform for adolescents to express themselves.

_____ 9. Adolescents are only able to talk to their friends on social media.

_____ 10. Social media can be used to sell consumer goods.

_____ 11. If your child is trustworthy, you have nothing to worry about.

_____ 12. Social media can be used for tips and inspiration in a wide variety of different interests.

Answer Key

1. **True:** Social media is one of the ways young people socialize. It is totally normal for them, and quite frankly they are the "odd ones" when they are not allowed to be on social media.

2. **True:** There is a lot of information on social media. It's how we know about current events, fashion trends, and even the latest shopping deals! It is no different for young people.

3. **False:** You most definitely should have access to all of your children's social media accounts. You do not need to constantly check in, but within reason, you should check on things.

4. **True:** You absolutely should be friends with your child on social media. This allows you to stay up on what is going on without imposing.

5. **False:** Although there is a lot of good on social media, there is also a lot of bad—and your child's brain has not yet developed enough to manage the extent of social media. Therefore, it is on you to stay informed and up to date. Their brain is unable to handle everything!

6. **False:** It is a federal crime to exchange images of minors who are under the age of 18. Law enforcement takes this very seriously. In addition, it demonstrates poor boundaries and a lack of self-respect. If nothing else, this *should* be used as a scare tactic.

7. **False:** There is real danger in social media, as kids can be subject to cyberbullying or catfishing (impersonating another person). It is important to have honest conversations with your kids about these dangers and to emphasize the importance of boundaries!

8. **True:** Social media is a way for adolescents to express themselves so long as it is done in an appropriate manner. Kids don't understand the future; their minds are focused on the here and now. When discussing social media with your child, use real life examples to assist in their understanding. Don't dictate; teach and lead by example.

9. **False:** Kids are able to communicate with just about anyone on social media, including strangers and predators. If your child is telling you otherwise, this is simply false.

10. **True:** The ability to sell items is one reason social media is so popular, as it is a platform to market yourself, your brand, and consumer goods. But there can also be a negative side to marketing, as these advertisements can be overwhelming and potentially involve scams.

11. **False:** Bad things happen to some of the most trustworthy people. Everyone should use caution when using social media. You can trust your child and still exercise caution.

12. **True:** The vastness of social media is one of the positive things it offers. Nearly every interest on the planet is represented and shared among a variety of posts, pages, and users. Social media is not all bad, so long as it is used with caution, boundaries, and thought. As a parent, it is on you to teach and model these things for your child.

Social Media Self-Care

Some of us spend too much time in the virtual world. Although it can be tempting to always be online, part of using social media responsibly is stepping back and being present in the real world instead of always living in the online world. This handout can remind you of ways you can use social media but also continue to take care of your mental and physical health. Add in your own ideas in the blank boxes provided!

Unfollow accounts that don't bring you comfort and positive feelings.	Go offline for a bit.	Set a schedule or limits to scrolling.
Turn off your notifications.	Remember your boundaries—it's okay to mute certain accounts.	You don't have to respond to every comment or message!

Other:

Other:

Justice and Equality

Justice and equality means that everyone is treated fairly and equally, regardless of their gender, race, sexuality, ethnicity, income, intelligence, and more. However, sometimes this isn't always our experience. This worksheet is designed to help you identify where you don't feel things are just or fair when it comes to your basic human needs.

Basic Human Needs	Is This Need Being Met? (Y/N)	Why or Why Not?	How Can This Need Be Met?
Belongingness: Do you feel like you belong in your community, at school, and in your family?			
Self-esteem: Do you feel good about yourself?			

Basic Human Needs	Is This Need Being Met? (Y/N)	Why or Why Not?	How Can This Need Be Met?
Safety and security: Do you feel safe both physically and emotionally?			
Freedom: Are you free to be who you are, think what you want to think, or say what you want to say?			
Identity: Do you feel accepted for all that you are (e.g., weight, language, race, ethnicity, religion, personality, physical appearance)			

Basic Human Needs	Is This Need Being Met? (Y/N)	Why or Why Not?	How Can This Need Be Met?
Cultural acceptance: Do you feel that society respects your culture's values, traditions, and rituals?			
Justice: Do you feel like you have equal opportunities?			
Personal fulfillment: Do you feel like you can be what you want to be? Do you feel like you matter and can participate in life?			

Ages 12+

My Identity

Your identity can be determined by many things, such as your ethnicity, race, personality, religion, and more. However, too often, people make assumptions about someone's identity based only on how that person looks, talks, or behaves. We all come with different colors, shapes, beliefs, cultures, and life experiences. In the frame below, write or draw a picture of your true identity. Think deeper than what's on the outside and include things that some people may not know about you.

Ages 15+

Privilege

Privilege is when some members of society have special opportunities or advantages because of their race, gender, sexual orientation, culture, income level, beliefs, and more. It is important to be aware of what privileges you have, how they benefit you, and how they may affect others. On the checklist below, identify any statements that are true for you.

☐ I am never uncomfortable socializing with others because of my race.

☐ I see people who are the same race as me on TV and in magazines.

☐ Privilege is not something my family talks about.

☐ I learn about people from my racial background when discussing national history.

☐ My school materials include people of my race.

☐ My family can easily afford a tutor or college coach if I am struggling academically.

☐ I can go into a music shop and find a music artist of my race represented.

☐ I can walk into a grocery store and find staple foods that fit with my cultural traditions.

☐ I can go into any hair salon and find someone who can cut or style my hair.

☐ I don't have to think about which bathroom I should use.

☐ I can protect myself from people who disagree with me or do not like me.

☐ People don't treat me differently based on the way I look or dress.

☐ My neighborhood is safe with little to no crime.

☐ My family never worries about where our next meal will come from.

☐ I am never asked to speak for all the people of my racial or ethnic group.

☐ People listen to my opinion despite my age.

☐ My teachers, coaches, and principals are the same race as me.

☐ My toys, dolls, books, and favorite TV shows have people of my race.

☐ I can find makeup to match my skin tone.

☐ All of the holidays I celebrate are recognized by our government, schools, etc.

☐ I can walk into a store and do whatever I want without someone questioning me.

☐ I plan to go to college.

☐ My family or I have a car to provide us with transportation.

☐ I am able to play sports and get a personal trainer if needed.

☐ I can practice my religious beliefs without fear of discrimination.

The more statements that you checked off, the more privilege you have. Having privilege is not bad, but it is something you need to be aware of. No one necessarily asks to be privileged, but it is unfair to use your privilege knowingly and to your advantage.

What Is Radical Acceptance?

Radical acceptance is about accepting reality when you encounter a difficult situation that is outside of your control. When you accept the situation, it doesn't mean you like it or approve of it—you simply acknowledge its existence, which can help you get unstuck. To practice radical acceptance, you first need to figure out if the situation is one you can control or if it's one you can work to change. Think of a recent situation that you're having a difficult time with and follow the diagram below to see where you end up!

Recent situation: _____

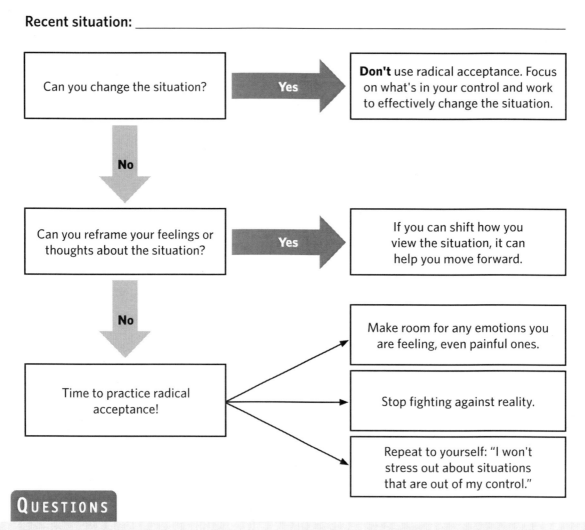

Can you change the situation? → **Yes** → **Don't** use radical acceptance. Focus on what's in your control and work to effectively change the situation.

No ↓

Can you reframe your feelings or thoughts about the situation? → **Yes** → If you can shift how you view the situation, it can help you move forward.

No ↓

Time to practice radical acceptance! →
- Make room for any emotions you are feeling, even painful ones.
- Stop fighting against reality.
- Repeat to yourself: "I won't stress out about situations that are out of my control."

QUESTIONS

- Practicing radical acceptance can be hard, especially when it comes to something you really wish were different. What has been something that is hard for you to accept?
- What are some situations in the future where you think you might need to use acceptance? Why?
- What are some situations you can think of where you should not use acceptance?

The Place of Acceptance

If you are having difficulty accepting something, take a few moments to think about the situation you are struggling with. Now, take a few deep breaths and begin to imagine what would look differently about your life *if* you were able to accept this situation. Make sure to use each of your five senses (sight, sound, smell, taste, and touch) to get a complete picture of your life in this place. Once you have that picture in your mind, use the following space to draw or write what that place looks like for you.

Closure

Often, life can take unexpected turns. Relationships end, school finishes, pandemics occur, or maybe things don't work out the way you expected them to. When this happens, finding closure becomes important so you can move forward and not live with regret, anger, or resentment. Closure can look different to different people—for some, it may involve having a hard conversation, while for others, it may be allowing themselves to feel a loss and grieve. The important part is figuring out what it looks like to you!

What is one situation that you are struggling to find closure with right now?

_____

_____

_____

What makes it hard for you to find closure with this situation?

_____

_____

_____

If you were able to find closure with this situation, what would that look like for you? Draw, paint, or write what you need for closure in the space provided (or you can use a separate sheet if you need more room):

Checking In and Out

It can be hard to remember how much work you have put into yourself, your relationships, and your overall well-being. This worksheet will help you track where you started versus where you are now so you can remember all the progress you have made. First, from the following list, circle three issues that you have been working on in your treatment.

Safety	Negative behaviors	School work	Shutting down	Sadness
Worry	Trust	Yelling	Anger	Listening
Self-harm	Fatigue	Boredom	Lying	Shame
Loneliness	Coping skills	Communication	Social media	Self-esteem
Self-respect	Confidence	Mindfulness	Acceptance	

Next, rate how you were struggling with each issue before treatment and how you are doing now (with 0 being "not struggling at all" and 10 being "struggling a lot").

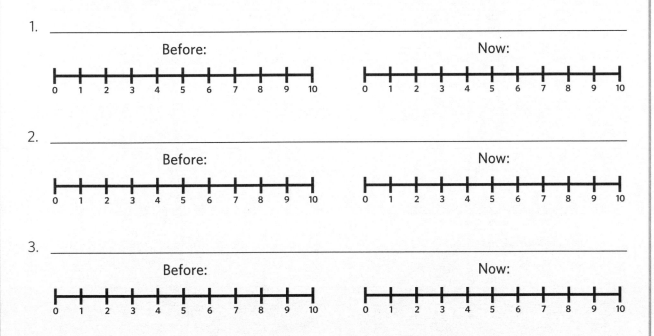

Finally, take a moment and validate the progress you have made in these three areas. You may not necessarily be where you want to be, but you are most likely closer than you were before. Keep going!"

Powerful Words

Ages 7+

It can be awkward saying nice things to yourself, especially when you're asked to do this in front of a mirror. However, it *works*! You've done amazing work, and we want to leave you with powerful words you can take with you. Complete the sentences in the mirror below and say them to yourself in front of your own bathroom or bedroom mirror every day. Seriously! Be as creative as you want—you can write these down on sticky notes or write directly on your mirror with a dry erase marker.

I am:

I will:

I can:

The Best Is Yet to Come

You should be so proud of all of your hard work! Let's take one final look at what you've learned about yourself and how you can move forward with more skills and a better understanding of who you are. Think about anything you may still need or are missing from this journey. Then imagine you have a magic wand that gave you everything you needed and answered all your questions! In the corresponding boxes, write or draw any questions you have as you think about your future and how you want it to look.

What is missing? What do I still need?	Questions I still have...

Acknowledgments

We were beyond excited when we got this opportunity! Each of us has worked timelessly and tirelessly to give you something that is innovative, helpful, and beneficial to children, adolescents, caregivers, treatment providers, and so many more. We want to thank our families and the long nights they allowed, the grace from our own clients, and the team that made this happen. Lastly, we want to thank you: the caregivers of the world! Without you, this world wouldn't be what it is. Keep up the hard work, take care of yourself, and ask for help when you need it!

About the Authors

Amanda K. Crowder, MSW, LCSW, graduated from the University of North Carolina at Charlotte with a BA in psychology and a master's in social work. She is a licensed clinical social worker in the state of North Carolina and the owner of Calming Waters Counseling Services. Amanda is an outstanding and well-respected therapist, author, and presenter. She is creative and entertaining and is an expert at moving evidence-based interventions into practical methods for application. She has created and adapted evidence-based interventions to work with the most challenging children, adolescents, and families in the most difficult situations. In addition, Amanda is a certified trauma therapist and certified EMDR therapist. Evaluations of her work have established her as someone who can break through resistant clients and family members to reduce symptoms and improve experiences. She has been successful working in multiple settings and has consistently delivered interventions that have resulted in client and family member engagement and improvement in accomplishing therapeutic goals. Amanda believes in the importance of the therapeutic relationship and creates a space to ensure her clients feel heard, safe, and seen. Amanda lives in Charlotte, NC with her son. She enjoys spending her time at the beach and with family and friends.

Julianna Elsworth, MSW, LCSW, is a graduate of Syracuse University's School of Social Work master's program. She completed her bachelor's degree in psychology and sociology with a minor in Spanish at St. John Fisher College in Rochester, NY. Julianna has spent much of her career providing therapy services to children, adolescents, and families in complex systems and in various settings. She has also had the pleasure of serving as an adjunct professor in the MSW program at Syracuse University and speaking for PESI, developing and providing trauma-informed training for school personnel.

Currently, Julianna is the clinical director and an outpatient therapist at Calming Waters Counseling Services in Charlotte, NC. She specializes in treating children and adolescents with complex trauma and PTSD, sexually reactive behavior, those struggling with familial conflict, and self-injurious behavior. She is a certified trauma specialist, is trained in EMDR, and provides clinical supervision to associatively licensed clinical social workers. She is passionate about improving the lives of others through treatment, teaching, advocacy, and relationships.

Julianna currently lives in Charlotte, NC, with her husband and two children. She considers herself a lifelong learner who is gratefully humbled to walk alongside people on their journey through life.

Anastasia Harmeyer, MSW, LCSW, LCAS, is a graduate of the University of North Carolina at Charlotte's master's program in social work. She also has a master's in criminal justice and completed her undergraduate degree in criminology and sociology with a minor in psychology at The Ohio State University. She is a licensed clinical social worker and a licensed clinical addictions specialist in the state of North Carolina.

Anastasia decided to pursue her master's in social work after working with adolescents in the criminal justice system and recognizing the significance of therapeutic services. She has also had the opportunity to serve as the clinical director of a community mental health and substance abuse organization, run full-fidelity DBT groups, and work as a trainer for PESI, facilitating two-day intensive DBT training.

Anastasia is currently an outpatient therapist at Calming Waters Counseling Services in Charlotte, NC. She specializes in working with adolescents and adults with borderline personality disorder, addiction, complex trauma and PTSD, relational conflict with couples and families, self-harming behaviors, and suicidality. She is trained in DBT and EMDR and is a certified clinical supervisor for provisionally licensed LCSWs. She is passionate about providing a supportive and validating therapeutic environment to assist her clients in building skills, balancing acceptance and change, and meeting their goals. Anastasia also has a deep love of animals and is passionate about advocating for both animals and humans; she believes that all are deserving of a life worth living.

Made in United States
Cleveland, OH
23 December 2024

12569221R00140